The Rainbow Book of Bible Stories

The Creation

THE RAINBOW BOOK OF

BIBLE STORIES

BY

J. HAROLD GWYNNE, D.D.

ILLUSTRATED BY

STEELE SAVAGE

CLEVELAND  NEW YORK

THE WORLD PUBLISHING COMPANY

Library of Congress Catalog Card Number: 56–9264

CW

Contents

FROM THE OLD TESTAMENT

I. Stories of the Hebrew Patriarchs

II. Stories About Moses and the Israelites

III. Stories About Joshua and the Judges

IV. Stories About Three Kings of United Israel

V. Stories About the Divided Kingdom

VI. Stories About the Jews in Captivity

FROM THE NEW TESTAMENT

I. The Four Gospels

II. The Book of Acts

FROM THE OLD TESTAMENT

*Moses broke the
tablets of the law*

I.

STORIES

OF THE

HEBREW

PATRIARCHS

Male and female He created them

ONE

God's Work of Creation

Genesis 1:1–2:9

IN THE beginning God created the heaven and the earth. That was a long, long time ago. How long ago, people do not agree. Many say we can never really know. But it is known that God existed before the world was made, and that He created all things by His wisdom and power.

At the very beginning, the earth was far different from the way it looks now. It was a formless mass; empty and blank and utterly void of life. Deep waters covered the surface of the earth, and complete darkness was everywhere. But the Spirit of God moved upon the face of the waters to bring order and beauty out of dark and fearful chaos.

God's work of creation extended, as we are told, over six days, to give us the familiar things of our world—day and night, the sky overhead, the oceans, and the dry land. Then came the fishes and the birds, the land animals, the people. Our world would be a strange place indeed if any one of the days of creation had been left out.

At first God said, "Let there be light." And light was created. God saw that it was good; and He divided the light from the darkness. And God called the light Day, and the darkness He called Night. And the evening and the morning were the first day of creation.

Next God said, "Let there be a firmament in the midst of the waters, to divide the waters above and below." So God made the beautiful sky, and created the clouds to carry the sky moisture above the water-covered earth be-

low. And God called the firmament Heaven. This was God's work of creation on the second day.

On the third day, God caused the waters to gather together in wide, deep places and called them Seas. He also caused dry land to appear, and called it Earth. And God saw that this was good. Then God said, "Let the earth bring forth plants, those producing seed, and fruit trees producing fruit which bears its own seed, each after its kind, upon the earth." And it was so. And God saw that it was good. And the evening and the morning were the third day of creation.

The fourth day God said, "Let there be lights in the firmament of the heaven to divide the day from the night; and let them be for signs and for seasons and for days and years, and let them be for lights in the heaven to give light upon the earth." And this came to pass. And God made two great lights, the sun to rule the day and the moon to rule the night; He made the stars also. And God saw that it was good. Thus ended the fourth day of creation.

On the fifth day God said, "Let the waters bring forth great numbers of moving creatures, and birds that may fly above the earth in the open firmament of heaven." So God created great whales and every living creature that swims in the waters, after its kind; and every flying bird after its kind. And God saw that it was good. And God blessed them, saying, "Be fruitful, and multiply, and fill the waters in the seas, and let birds multiply in the earth." And the evening and the morning were the fifth day of creation.

On the sixth day God said, "Let the earth bring forth living creatures after their kinds: cattle, and creeping things, and beasts of the earth." And it was so. And God saw that it was good.

But God's highest creative work was yet to come. For God said, "Let us make man in our image, after our likeness; and let him have dominion over the fish of the sea, and over the birds of the air, and over the cattle, and over all the earth, and over every creeping thing that creeps upon the earth." So God created man in his own image; male and female He created them. And God blessed them and said, "Be fruitful and multiply, and replenish the earth and subdue it; and have dominion over the fish of the sea, and over the birds of the air, and over every living thing that moves upon the earth."

And God said to man, "Behold, I have given you every plant producing seed which is upon the face of the earth, and every tree producing fruit which bears its own seed; they shall be yours for food. And to every beast of the earth, and to every bird of the air, and to everything that creeps upon the earth, everything in which there is life, I have given all green plants for food." And it was so. And God saw everything that He had made, and behold, it was very good. And this completed the sixth day of creation.

Thus the heaven and the earth were finished, and all the host of them. And God rested on the seventh day from all the work which He had done. And God blessed the seventh day, and sanctified it, because on it He rested from all the work of creation which He had done.

The Lord God had formed man of the dust of the ground, and had breathed into his nostrils the breath of life; so that man became a living being. Then the Lord God planted a garden to the east in Eden; and there the Lord God put the man whom He had created. And out of the ground in the garden of Eden the Lord God made grow every tree that is pleasant to the sight and good for food. There was also the tree of life growing in the midst of the garden, and the tree of knowledge of good and evil. Thus, in this happy paradise, the first man and the first woman dwelt in fellowship and communion with the God who had created them.

TWO

The Transgression of Adam and Eve

Genesis 2:10–3:24

ARIVER flowed out of Eden to water the garden, and from there it divided into four branches. The first was named Pison, and it flowed around the whole land of Havilah, where there was much fine gold and bdellium and onyx stone. The name of the second river was Gihon, and it flowed around the whole land of Ethiopia. The third river, named Hiddekel, flowed to the east of Assyria. And the fourth river was the great river Euphrates.

The Lord God took the man and put him in the garden of Eden to cultivate it and keep it. And the Lord God commanded the man, saying, "You are free to eat of every tree of the garden; but you shall not eat of the tree of the knowledge of good and evil, for in the day that you eat of it you shall die."

Then the Lord God said, "It is not good that the man should be alone; I will make him a helpmeet to be a companion for him."

In the meantime the Lord God formed out of the ground every beast of the field and every bird of the air, and brought them to Adam to see what he would call them; and whatever Adam called each living creature, that was its name. So Adam gave names to all cattle, and to the birds of the air, and to every beast of the field. But for Adam there was not found a suitable mate.

So the Lord God caused a deep sleep to fall upon Adam, and while he slept took one of his ribs and closed up the empty space with flesh. And from the rib which the Lord God had taken from man He made a woman and brought her to the man.

And Adam said, "This is now bone of my bones and flesh of my flesh; she shall be called Woman, because she was taken out of Man." Therefore, according to God's plan, a man shall leave his father and mother and cleave to his wife, and they shall be as one flesh. And both man and woman were naked, but in their state of purity and innocence they were not ashamed.

But, alas, the man and the woman did not long remain in this state of purity and innocence. They were soon to disobey God's commandment and commit evil. This is the way it came about.

The serpent was more crafty than any beast of the field which the Lord God had made. One day in the garden the serpent said to the woman, "Has not God indeed said, 'You shall not eat of every tree of the garden'?" And the woman said to the serpent, "We are permitted to eat of the fruit of the trees of the garden; but of the tree which is in the midst of the garden God said, 'You are not to eat of its fruit nor to touch it; if you do, you will die.'"

But the serpent, telling a lie, said to the woman, "You will not really die. For God knows that whenever you eat of it your eyes will be opened and you will be as gods, knowing good and evil."

So the woman was deceived and yielded to temptation. When she saw that the tree was good for food, and that it was pleasant to the

17

eyes, and a tree to be desired to make one wise, she took some of its fruit and ate; and also gave some to her husband, and he ate. And the eyes of them both were opened, and they knew that they were naked, and for the first time they felt ashamed. To cover their nakedness they sewed fig leaves together and made themselves aprons.

Then, to their dismay, they heard the voice of the Lord God in the garden in the cool of the day, and Adam and his wife hid themselves from the presence of the Lord God among the trees of the garden. But the Lord God called to Adam, and said to him, "Where are you?" And Adam said, "I heard your voice in the garden and I was afraid, because I was naked; and I hid myself."

The Lord God said to Adam, "Who told you that you were naked? Have you eaten the fruit of the tree of which I commanded you, 'You shall not eat of it'?" Adam, seeking to excuse himself from blame, replied, "The woman whom you gave to be with me gave me some of the fruit of the tree, and I ate." Then the Lord God said to the woman, "What is this wicked thing that you have done?" The woman, seeking to excuse herself, said, "The serpent beguiled and tempted me, and I ate."

Then the Lord God said to the serpent, "Because you have done this, you are cursed above all cattle, and above every beast of the field; you shall crawl upon your belly, and you shall eat dust all the days of your life. I will cause enmity between you and the woman, and between your progeny and her progeny. The progeny of the woman shall bruise your head, and you shall bruise their heel."

To the woman God said, "I will greatly multiply your travail in childbearing; in pain and suffering shall you bring forth children; also your desire shall be for your husband, and he shall rule over you."

And to Adam the Lord said, "Because you have heeded the voice of your wife, and have eaten of the tree of which I commanded you, 'You shall not eat of it,' cursed is the ground on your account; in labor and sorrow you shall eat of it all the days of your life; thorns and thistles it shall bring forth to trouble you; and you shall eat the plants of the field. In the sweat of your face you shall eat bread till you return to the ground, for out of it you were taken; you are made from the dust, and to dust you shall return."

Adam called his wife's name Eve, because she was the mother of all living. And for Adam and Eve the Lord God made garments of skins, and clothed them.

And the Lord God said, "Behold, the man has become as one of us, in that he knows good and evil; and now, in order that he may not put forth his hand and take also of the tree of life, and eat, and live forever, I will send him forth from the garden of Eden, to till the ground from which he was taken."

So the Lord God drove the man out from his garden of paradise. And at the east of the garden of Eden the Lord placed Cherubims, and a flaming sword which turned in all directions, to guard the way of the tree of life.

The Lord God drove them out from his garden of paradise

THREE

Cain Slays His Brother Abel

Genesis 4:1–26

THE first son born to Adam and Eve, after they were expelled from the garden of Eden, was named Cain. At the time of his birth, Eve, the first mother, said, "I have given birth to a son, due to the presence of the Lord." Some time later Eve gave birth to a second son whom she called Abel.

The years passed, and the brothers Cain and Abel grew up and became young men. Abel became a shepherd and took care of flocks of sheep. Cain became a tiller of the ground and raised different crops that grow in the earth.

In time Cain brought the Lord an offering of the fruit of the ground which he had harvested. At the same time Abel brought the Lord an offering of the firstlings of his flock of sheep and of their fat. And the Lord accepted and received Abel and his offering, but Cain and his offering were not acceptable to the Lord. There was something about Cain's life and spirit which the Lord did not approve.

Cain became very angry when his offering was not accepted, and his countenance became dark and sullen. The Lord said to Cain, "Why are you angry, and why has your countenance darkened? If you do well, will you not be accepted? And if you do not do well, sin lies at the door; it desires you, but you shall rule over it."

But Cain did not heed the word of the Lord.

He continued to brood in anger and envy against his brother Abel. And one day, when Cain and Abel were in the field, Cain suddenly rose up against his brother, struck him with a heavy club, and killed him.

And the Lord said to Cain, the first murderer, "Where is Abel your brother?" The guilty man replied, "I do not know; am I my brother's keeper?" And the Lord said, "What have you done? The voice of your brother's blood cries to me from the ground. And now you are cursed from the earth, which has opened her mouth to receive your brother's blood from your hand. When you till the ground it shall no longer yield to you its strength; you shall be a fugitive and a vagabond in the earth."

Then the remorseful Cain said to the Lord, "My punishment is greater than I can bear. Behold, you have driven me out today from the face of the earth; and from your face I shall be hidden; and I shall be a fugitive and a vagabond in the earth, and everyone who finds me will want to slay me."

But the Lord said to him, "This shall not be. Whoever slays Cain shall be revenged sevenfold." And the Lord set a mark on Cain, lest any who encountered him should kill him. Then Cain left the presence of the Lord, and dwelt in the land of Nod, which means "wandering," to the east of Eden.

After the death of her second son Abel, Eve

Cain slew his brother Abel

gave birth to a third son whom she called Seth. "For God," Eve said, "has given me another son instead of Abel, whom Cain slew." In due time, to Seth also was born a son, whom he called Enos. From that time men began to call upon the name of the Lord in prayer and worship. Thus Seth became the father of the godly line of descendants of whom Noah was born.

FOUR

Noah Builds the Ark

Genesis 6:1–8:22

WHEN men began to multiply on the earth, and daughters were born to them, the young men saw that these daughters were fair; and they chose them to become their wives.

As time went on, the world became filled with evil. And God saw that the wickedness of man was great in the earth, and that the imagination of man's heart was only continuously evil. And the Lord regretted that he had made man on the earth, and it grieved his heart. And the Lord said, "I will destroy man, whom I have created, from the face of the earth, man and beast and creeping things and birds of the air, for I regret that I have made them."

One of the descendants of Seth, after many generations had passed, was Noah, the son of Lamech. Noah was a just man, and guiltless in his generation because he walked with God. He had three sons, Shem, Ham, and Japheth. And Noah found favor in the eyes of the Lord. God said to Noah, "I am going to destroy all living creatures, for the earth is filled with violence through them; behold, I will destroy them with the earth. Therefore build an ark of gopher wood; make rooms in the ark, and seal it inside and out with pitch."

Then the Lord instructed Noah to make the ark four hundred and fifty feet long, seventy-five feet wide, and forty-five feet high. A window was to be built for the ark; a door was to be set in one side; and the ark was to have lower, second, and third stories.

The Lord told Noah, "Behold, I will bring a flood of waters upon the earth, to destroy all flesh, in which is the breath of life, from under heaven; everything that is in the earth shall die. But with you I will establish my covenant; and you shall come into the ark, you, and your sons, and your wife, and your sons' wives with you."

The Lord commanded Noah further, saying, "Of every living thing of all flesh, you shall bring two of every sort, male and female, into the ark, to keep them alive with you. Of birds after their kind, and of cattle after their kind, of every creeping thing of the earth after its kind, two of every sort shall come to you to keep them alive. And take with you all food that is eaten, and store it away, and it shall be

And in the dove's mouth was a newly plucked olive leaf

food for you and for them." Thus Noah did all that God commanded him to do.

Then the Lord commanded Noah to enter into the ark with all the members of his family, eight persons in all. And Noah and his wife and his three sons and their wives went into the ark, to escape the flood which was to be upon the earth. And according to God's commandment, Noah took with him into the ark seven pairs of all clean animals, male and female; a pair of unclean animals, male and female; and seven pairs of the birds of the air, male and female. These all went two by two with Noah into the ark.

And after seven days the waters of the flood came upon the earth. On the seventeenth day of the second month all the fountains of the great deep burst forth, and the windows of heaven were opened. And torrents of rain fell upon the earth for forty days and forty nights. But Noah and his family were safely sheltered and protected in the ark.

As the flood continued upon the earth, the waters increased and bore up the ark; and it was lifted up above the earth, where it floated on the face of the waters. And the waters prevailed greatly upon the earth; and all the high mountains were covered over with many feet of water.

And all flesh died that moved upon the earth, birds, cattle, beasts, and every creeping thing that crept upon the earth, and every man; every living thing on the earth perished in the flood of waters. Only Noah and those that were with him in the ark were alive and safe. And the flood lasted for a hundred and fifty days.

But God remembered Noah and all the living creatures that were with him in the ark. And God made a wind blow over the earth, and the waters subsided; the fountains of the deep and the windows of heaven were stopped, and the rain from heaven was restrained, and the waters receded from the earth continually. And after a hundred and fifty days the waters were abated; and the ark came to rest, in the seventh month, on the seventeenth day of the month, upon the mountains of Ararat. And the waters decreased continually until the tenth month; on the first day of that month the tops of the mountains were visible.

At the end of forty days Noah opened the window of the ark which he had made, and sent forth a raven, which went to and fro until the waters were dried up from the earth. He also sent forth a dove, to see if the waters had abated from the face of the earth. But the dove found no place to rest her foot, and returned to the ark, for the waters were still upon the face of the whole earth. Then Noah stretched forth his hand and pulled the dove back into the ark with him.

Noah waited another seven days, and again sent forth the dove from the ark. And the dove returned in the evening, and lo, in her mouth she had a newly plucked olive leaf. So Noah knew that the waters had abated from the earth. He waited then yet another seven days, and sent forth the dove a third time; this time it did not return again.

In the first day of the first month of the new year, the waters were dried from off the earth; and Noah removed the covering of the ark and looked out, and behold, the ground was dry. On the twenty-seventh day of the second month, the earth was completely dry.

Then God spoke to Noah, saying, "Go forth from the ark, you, and your wife, and your sons, and your sons' wives with you. Bring forth with you every living thing that is with you, of all flesh—the birds, the beasts, and every creeping thing that creeps upon the earth—so that they may breed abundantly upon the earth, and be fruitful and multiply upon the earth." So Noah went forth, and the members of his family with him. Every beast, every creeping thing, and every bird, everything that creeps upon the earth, after its kind, went forth out of the ark.

And in that fresh, clean, new world, Noah built an altar to the Lord, and took of every clean beast and of every clean bird, and offered burnt offerings on the altar. And the Lord smelled the sweet savor of Noah's offering, and said in his heart, "I will never again curse the ground on man's account, even though the imagination of man's heart is evil from his youth; neither will I ever again destroy all living things, as I have done. While the earth remains, seed time and harvest, cold and heat, summer and winter, and day and night shall not cease."

And God established a covenant with Noah and his descendants that He would never again destroy all flesh upon the earth by the waters of a great flood. And as a token of this everlasting covenant, God set a beautiful rainbow in the clouds of the sky.

FIVE

The Tower of Babel

Genesis 10:1–11:9

AFTER the flood, the three sons of Noah —Shem, Ham, and Japheth— raised large families of sons and daughters. These families in turn increased and multiplied into tribes and nations, which spread abroad into different lands and developed different languages. Thus the descendants of Shem, Ham, and Japheth formed the various peoples and nations that we read about in later Bible history.

In the early period of new beginnings after the flood, the whole earth had but one language. And it came to pass, as men came from the east, that they found a plain in the land of Shinar, or Babylonia, and settled there. After a time they said to one another, "Come, let us make bricks and bake them thoroughly." And they made great quantities of bricks to use for stone, and learned how they could use mud for mortar.

Then these dwellers in Shinar said, "Let us come together and build ourselves a city, and a tower whose top will reach to heaven, and let us make a name for ourselves, lest we be scattered abroad upon the face of the whole earth." So all the people began to build. Many brick houses were erected for the people to live in. But the greatest undertaking was the huge tower which rose to a great height above the plain of Shinar. The people thought this tower would be a great and lasting monument to their industry and ingenuity.

But their selfish pride in this vast undertaking displeased the God of heaven. And the Lord came down to see the city and the tower which the children of men had built.

A tower whose top will reach to heaven

And the Lord said, "Behold, they are all one people and they all speak one language; and this is only the beginning of what they intend to do; now nothing which they imagine will be impossible for them to carry out. Come, we will go down, and there confound their language, so that they may not be able to understand one another's speech."

So the Lord of heaven and earth confounded their language by causing them to speak with different tongues, so that they could not understand one another. And the Lord scattered them abroad from the plain of Shinar over the face of all the earth, and they left off building the city. And the tall tower remained unfinished.

Therefore the name of the tower was called Babel, which means "the place of God's judgment," because there the Lord confounded the language of all the earth; and from there the Lord scattered the people of Babylonia into other regions of the earth.

SIX

God's Call and Promise to Abraham

Genesis 11:27–12:20

THE life story of Abraham is one of the most important of all the Old Testament stories, for it marks the beginning of a new era in human history and in God's plan of redemption. Abraham was the son of Terah, forefather of the Hebrew people, father of the faithful, friend of God.

Terah lived in the city of Ur in the land of Chaldea. He had three sons, Abraham, Nahor, and Haran. Terah was seventy years old when Abraham was born. Haran, who was the father of Lot, died in the land of his birth before his father Terah. Abraham married a wife by the name of Sarai, and Nahor married a woman by the name of Milcah.

Desiring to get away from the evil influence of heathen idolatry in Ur of Chaldea, Terah took his family and went forth to go into the land of Canaan. In the family group were Terah, Abraham and Sarai, and Lot, Terah's grandson, the son of Haran. They journeyed northward through the valley of the Euphrates River until they came to the land of Haran, where they settled for a time. Some time later Terah died in Haran; he did not live to reach the land of Canaan.

While Abraham continued to sojourn in Haran, the Lord God spoke to him and said, "Go forth from your own country and your own kindred and your father's house to the land that I will show you. And I will make of your descendants a great nation, and I will bless you, and make your name great, and you will be a blessing. I will bless those who bless you, and curse anyone who curses you; and through you all the families of the earth will be blessed."

So by faith Abraham set forth as the Lord had told him; and Lot went with him. Abra-

Abraham and his family came to the land of Canaan

ham was seventy-five years old when he departed from Haran. And Abraham took with him Sarai his wife, and Lot his brother's son, and all the persons and possessions which they had gathered in Haran; and they went forth on the long journey to the land of Canaan. Their long trek led them across mountains, deserts, and rivers over the westward route that led through Damascus, and southward to Canaan. After perhaps a year of toilsome travel and many adventures, they finally came to the land of Canaan. And Abraham and his family passed through the land until they came to the place called Sichem, to the plain of Moreh. At that time the Canaanites were still in the land.

There the Lord appeared to Abraham and said, "To your posterity I will give this land." So Abraham built an altar there to the Lord, who had appeared to him. From there Abraham removed to a mountain on the east of Bethel, and pitched his tent, with Bethel on the west and Hai on the east. And there also Abraham built an altar to the Lord and called upon the name of the Lord. Soon Abraham journeyed on, still going toward the south.

It came to pass that there was a famine in the land of Canaan, and Abraham went down into Egypt to escape the famine. When they were nearing Egypt, Abraham said to Sarai his wife, "I know that you are a beautiful woman; therefore, when the Egyptians see you, they will say that you are my wife; and they will want to kill me so that they may take you for themselves. Therefore tell them that you are my sister, so that it may go well with me on your account, and my life may be spared because of you."

When Abraham came into Egypt the Egyptians saw that Sarai was indeed very beautiful. The princes of Pharaoh also saw her, and sang her praises to Pharaoh. And Sarai was taken into Pharaoh's house. And for her sake Pharaoh treated Abraham well; and gave him presents of sheep and cattle, and menservants and maidservants to serve him.

But the Lord sent great plagues upon Pharaoh and his household because of Sarai, Abraham's wife. So Pharaoh called Abraham, and said to him, "Why have you done this to me? Why did you not tell me that Sarai was your wife? Why did you pretend that she was your sister, so that I could take her for my wife? Now then, here is your wife, take her, and go your way." And Pharaoh issued orders to his men concerning Abraham; and they sent him away, with his wife and family and all his flocks and herds.

And Abraham went up out of the land of Egypt, he and his wife, his nephew Lot, and all that he had, and they came again into the southern country called the Negeb.

SEVEN

God's Covenant With Abraham

Genesis 15:1–21; 17:15–21; 21:1–8

WHILE Abraham was living near the oaks of Mamre near Hebron, the word of the Lord came to him in a vision, saying, "Fear not, Abraham, I am your shield and your exceedingly great reward." And Abraham said, "Lord God, what will you give me, seeing that I am childless, and that my servant Eliezer of Damascus is the only heir of my house?" And Abraham spoke further to the Lord, saying, "Behold, you have given me no child; and a servant born in my house is my heir."

And behold, the word of the Lord came to Abraham, saying, "The one you speak of shall not be your heir; but your own son shall be your heir." And the Lord brought Abraham out of his tent at night and said, "Look upward to heaven and count the stars, if you are able." Then God said to Abraham, "Your descendants shall likewise be innumerable." And Abraham believed the word of the Lord; and the Lord reckoned it to him as righteousness.

And God said to Abraham, "I am the Lord who brought you out of Ur in the land of Chaldea, to give you this new land to inherit." Abraham replied, "Lord God, how shall I know that I am to inherit it?" The Lord said to Abraham, "Bring before me now a heifer three years old, a she-goat three years old, a ram three years old, a turtledove, and a young pigeon." Abraham brought all these as directed, cut them in half, and laid each piece one against the other; but the birds he did not cut in half. And when vultures came down upon the carcasses, Abraham drove them away.

As the sun was going down, a deep sleep fell upon Abraham; and lo, a fear of great darkness came upon him. Then the Lord said to Abraham, "Know of a certainty that your descendants will be strangers in a land that is not theirs, and will be servants and slaves there, and will be oppressed and afflicted for four hundred years. But I will bring to judgment the nation which they serve, and in due time they will come forth with great possessions. And you shall be gathered to your fathers in peace; you shall be buried in a good old age. And your descendants shall come here again in the fourth generation; for the iniquity of the Amorites is not yet full and complete."

When the sun had gone down and it was dark, behold, a smoking furnace and a burning lamp passed between the offerings that Abraham had arranged. On that day the Lord made a covenant with Abraham, saying, "To your posterity I will give this land, from the river Nile in Egypt to the great river Euphrates; it is the land now occupied by the Kenites, the Kenizzites, the Kadmonites, the Hittites, the Perizzites, the Rephaims, the Amorites, the Canaanites, the Girgashites, and the Jebusites."

Now Sarai, Abraham's wife, bore him no children. But God said to Abraham, "In re-

The word of the Lord came to Abraham

gard to Sarai your wife, you shall no longer call her Sarai, but Sarah shall be her name. I will bless her, and also give you a son by her; yes, I will bless her, and she shall be a mother of nations; kings of peoples shall be born of her." Then Abraham fell on his face and laughed, and said to himself, "Shall a child indeed be born to me when I am a hundred years old. And shall Sarah, who is ninety years old, give birth to a child?" But God reaffirmed His promise: "Your wife Sarah shall indeed bear you a son, and you shall call his name Isaac; and I will establish my covenant with him for an everlasting covenant, and with his progeny after him."

The Lord visited Sarah as he had said, and the Lord did to Sarah as he had promised. And Sarah bore Abraham a son in his old age at the very time of which God had spoken to him. And Abraham named his son Isaac. And Abraham circumcised his son Isaac when he was eight days old, as God had commanded him. Abraham was a hundred years old when Isaac was born. And Sarah said, "God has given me laughter; and all who hear will laugh with me." The child grew, and was weaned; and Abraham made a great feast on the very day that Isaac was weaned, in gratitude to God for blessing them with this son of the covenant.

EIGHT

Abraham Offers Up Isaac

Genesis 22:1–19

WHEN Isaac became a young man, about twenty-five years old, God chose to test Abraham's faith in a most severe manner. God said to him, "Abraham"; and Abraham said, "Behold, here am I!" And God said, "Take now your son, your only son Isaac, whom you love so well, and go forth into the land of Moriah, and offer him there as a burnt offering upon one of the mountains of which I shall tell you."

Abraham was deeply perplexed and troubled by this command of the Lord, but he was ready to trust God fully and to obey His will. So Abraham arose early the next morning, saddled his ass, and took his son Isaac with

him, and also two of his young menservants. Abraham cut a bundle of wood to be used for the burnt offering and took it with him also. Then he set forth on the journey to the place of which God had told him.

Then, on the third day of the journey, Abraham lifted up his eyes and saw the place afar off. And Abraham said to his young men, "Wait here with the ass; I and the lad Isaac will go yonder and worship, and presently come back again to you."

And Abraham took the bundle of wood for the burnt offering, and laid it on the back of Isaac his son to carry; and Abraham took in his own hand the fire and a knife. So Isaac went forth carrying on his back the wood for

Abraham took the knife to slay his son Isaac

his own sacrifice. Thus the father and son went on together.

Isaac said to Abraham his father, "My father"; and Abraham said, "Here am I, my son." Then Isaac said, "Behold the fire and the wood; but where is the lamb for a burnt offering?" Abraham replied, "My son, God will provide himself with a lamb for a burnt offering." So they journeyed on together.

When they came to the place on Mount Moriah of which God had told him, Abraham built an altar there, and laid the wood in order, and bound Isaac his son, and laid him on the altar upon the wood. And Abraham stretched forth his hand, and took the knife to slay his son. But the angel of the Lord called to him from heaven and said, "Abraham, Abraham"; and Abraham said, "Here am I." The angel said, "Do not lay your hand on the lad or harm him in any way; for now I know that you fear God, since you have not withheld your son, your only son, whom you love so well, from me."

And Abraham lifted up his eyes and looked, and behold, behind him was a ram, caught in a thicket by his horns. And Abraham went and took the ram, and offered it up as a burnt offering instead of his son. That is why Abraham called the name of that place Jehovah-jireh, which means "the Lord will provide." And in all the years following, the Hebrews continued to speak of that place, saying, "On the mount of the Lord it shall be provided." Over a thousand years later, Solomon built the temple of God upon Mount Moriah, the place where Abraham had offered up his son Isaac.

God commended Abraham for his faith and obedience, and reaffirmed the covenant that He had made with him at Hebron. For the angel of the Lord called to Abraham from heaven a second time and said, "The Lord says, 'By myself I have sworn, that because you have done this thing, and have not withheld your son, your only son, whom you love so well, I will bless you, and I will multiply your progeny as the stars of the heaven and as the sand which is on the seashore. And your descendants shall possess the gate of their enemies, and through your descendants shall all the nations of the earth be blessed, because you have obeyed my voice.'"

So Abraham returned with Isaac to his young men, and they arose and went together to Beer-sheba; and Abraham dwelt at Beer-sheba.

NINE

Isaac Marries Rebekah

Genesis 24:1–67

THE years passed by and Isaac's mother Sarah died at the age of a hundred and twenty-seven years and was buried in the field of Machpelah, near Hebron in the land of Canaan. Abraham was also very old and was drawing near the end of his earthly journey. Before he died, he desired to see his son Isaac married to a woman of his own people.

So Abraham called his oldest and most trusted servant to him, and required an oath of him to the effect that he would help Isaac find a wife from his own people in Mesopotamia, and discourage him from taking a wife from the daughters of the Canaanites. Abraham also insisted that Isaac's wife should come back with him to live in the land which God had promised to Abraham and his descendants. So the old servant gave his solemn oath to Abraham that he would carry out his master's wishes in the matter.

Then the servant chose ten of Abraham's camels and departed, taking with him many gifts from his master. And he set forth on his journey and went to the city of Nahor in Mesopotamia. And he made the camels kneel down outside the city by a well of water at the time of evening when it was customary for the women to go out to draw water.

And the old servant prayed, "O Lord, God of my master Abraham, I pray you, give your servant good luck today, and show your loving-kindness to my master Abraham. Behold, I am standing here by the well of water, and the daughters of the men of the city are coming out to draw water. Let it happen that the maiden to whom I shall say, 'Let down your pitcher, I pray you, so that I may drink,' and who shall say, 'Drink, and I will let your camels drink also—let her be the one whom you have appointed for your servant Isaac. By this I shall know that you have shown your loving-kindness to my master."

Before the servant had finished praying, behold, Rebekah, the daughter of Bethuel, the son of Nahor, Abraham's brother, came out with her pitcher upon her shoulder. And she was a very beautiful young maiden. She went down to the well, and filled her pitcher, and came up again. The servant ran to meet her and said, "Let me, I pray you, drink a little water from your pitcher." With a smile Rebekah replied, "Drink, my lord"; and she promptly let down her pitcher upon her hand and gave him a drink. When she had finished giving him a drink she said, "I will draw water for your camels too, until they have had enough to drink." And she promptly emptied her pitcher into the trough and ran again to the well to draw water, and she drew enough for all his camels. The old servant gazed at Rebekah without saying a word, anxious to discover whether the Lord had rendered his journey successful or not.

The servant then gave Rebekah a gold earring, and two gold bracelets for her wrists, and inquired about herself and her family. When he learned that she was a relative of Abraham's, he blessed God for leading him to his master's own people.

Then Rebekah ran and told her mother's household about these things. When Rebekah's brother Laban saw the expensive gifts his sister had received, he ran out to the man still waiting by the well and invited him to come and lodge in his house. Laban also ungirded the camels and prepared a place for them to rest and eat. When the servant came into the house, food was set before him, but he declined to eat until he had explained his errand.

Then he related to Rebekah's family the whole story of how his master Abraham had sent him to seek a wife for his son Isaac. He described how the Lord, in answer to his prayer, had led him to them through the kindness and help of Rebekah.

Then Laban and Bethuel answered, "The thing comes from the Lord; we cannot speak to you bad or good. Behold, Rebekah is be-

Abraham's servant asked Rebekah for a drink from her pitcher

fore you; take her and go, and let her be your master's son's wife, as the Lord has spoken."

When Abraham's servant heard their words, he bowed himself to the earth and worshiped the Lord. And he brought forth jewels of silver and jewels of gold, and clothing, and gave them to Rebekah. He also gave precious ornaments to her brother and to her mother. And he and the men who were with him ate and drank, and stayed the night.

When they arose in the morning, the servant said, "Send me back again to my master." But Rebekah's mother and brother said, "Let the maiden stay with us a few days longer, at least ten; after that she may go." But the servant said, "Do not make me wait, since the Lord has prospered my way; let me return at once to my master." Then they called Rebekah, and said to her, "Are you willing to go with this man?" She humbly replied, "I will go." So they sent away Rebekah their sister and her nurse, and Abraham's servant and his men. The servant prepared camels for Rebekah and her maidservants to ride on, and so they began the journey back to Abraham.

Meanwhile Isaac had come from the well Lahai-roi and was living in the south country. One evening Isaac went out in the field to meditate; and he lifted up his eyes and saw camels approaching. So he started out to meet whoever was coming. And Rebekah lifted up her eyes, and when she saw Isaac, she alighted from the camel, and said to the servant, "Who is that man coming across the field to meet us?" The servant said, "It is my master." Therefore Rebekah discreetly took her veil and covered her face.

And the servant told Isaac everything that he had done, in keeping with Abraham's request. Then Isaac brought Rebekah into his tent, and she became his wife; and he loved her. Thus Isaac was comforted after his mother's death. And God's covenant with Abraham was renewed through Isaac.

TEN

How Jacob Secured Esau's Birthright

Genesis 25:1–34

ABRAHAM was a hundred and seventy-five years old when he died and was gathered to his people. His sons Isaac and Ishmael buried him in the cave of Machpelah, where Sarah his wife was buried. After the death of Abraham God blessed his son Isaac. Isaac was dwelling by the well Lahai-roi.

Isaac was forty years old when he married Rebekah, the daughter of Bethuel the Syrian of Padan-aram. For twenty years after they were married, Isaac and Rebekah did not have any children to bless their home. This was a great disappointment to them, and Isaac prayed to the Lord and begged Him to send them a child.

The Lord heard Isaac's prayer, and in due time Rebekah found that she was going to have a child. In fact, Rebekah was to become the mother of twin boys.

Before her twin sons were born, Rebekah was quite ill and wondered whether she was going to live. She prayed to the Lord about her trouble, and the Lord said to her, "You shall give birth to two nations, and these shall be divided; the one people shall be stronger than the other, and the elder shall serve the younger."

When the time came, Rebekah gave birth to twin sons. Although the boys were twins, they were not at all alike. The first-born son, who was named Esau, was covered with soft red hair. He was called Esau because that name means "hairy." The twin brother was born right afterward; his little hand had taken hold of Esau's heel, so that he was called Jacob, which means "he seizes by the heel" or "he supplants." The father Isaac was sixty years old when his twin sons were born.

When Esau and Jacob grew up to be young men they were very unlike each other in appearance, character, and interests. Esau loved the out-of-doors. He roamed the fields and woods in search of wild animals and became a skillful hunter of all sorts of wild game. With his bow and arrows he killed many wild animals and brought the tasty meat home for his family to eat. His father Isaac was very fond of the tasty meat which Esau provided, and for this reason Esau was his favorite son.

Jacob was a quiet, thoughtful man who did not care for the kind of outdoor life that Esau loved. Jacob liked to stay at home and enjoy the shelter and comforts of their spacious tents. He was a home-loving youth and helped his mother with the tasks that had to be done each day. So Rebekah came to be very partial to her son Jacob.

Once when Esau was away on a hunting trip, Jacob stayed at home and boiled a mess of pottage made of lentils. Esau had been gone for some time, and when he came back from hunting he was faint with hunger. Smelling the savory pottage which Jacob was cooking, he exclaimed, "Give me, I pray you, some of your red pottage to eat, for I am faint with

Jacob gave Esau food in exchange for his birthright

hunger!" When lentils are cooked they make a red pottage; so after this Esau was called Edom, which means "red."

Jacob had been waiting for an opportunity to take advantage of his brother Esau. The birthright belonged to Esau because he was the oldest son. This meant that he was entitled to a larger share of his father's possessions than Jacob. More important than that, it meant that the promises and blessings of the covenant which God had made with Abraham and Isaac would be passed on to the oldest son. Jacob wanted the birthright that belonged to Esau, and now he thought he had a good opportunity to take it from his unsuspecting brother.

So Jacob said to the famished Esau, "You must first sell me your birthright." Esau should have refused to consider it, but in his rough and carefree manner he replied, "I am on the point of death; what good will this birthright be to me?" Jacob wanted to make sure that Esau would not change his mind after he had satisfied his hunger, so he said, "Swear to me first that you will give me your birthright." So Esau took an oath and sold his birthright to Jacob. Then Jacob gave Esau bread and pottage of lentils. Esau ate and drank hungrily and greedily, and then rose up and went on his way again. Thus Esau despised his birthright, and surrendered it to his brother Jacob.

ELEVEN

Jacob Obtains Isaac's Blessing

Genesis 27:1–28:5

WHEN Isaac grew old and his eyes became dim so that he could not see, he called Esau his elder son, and said to him, "My son"; and Esau replied, "Here I am, father." Isaac said, "Behold, I am now old; I do not know the day of my death. Therefore, take your weapons, your quiver and your bow, and go out to the field and hunt for venison, and prepare for me the kind of savory meat that I love, and bring it to me so that I may eat of it, and bless you before I die."

Rebekah overheard what Isaac said to his son Esau. So when Esau went to the field to hunt for venison to bring to his father, Re-

bekah told her son Jacob what Isaac was planning to do. Then she said to Jacob, "My son, you must do what I command you. Go at once to the flock and bring me two good kids, and I will prepare from them the kind of savory meat for your father that he loves; and you shall take it to your father to eat, so that he may bless you before he dies."

Jacob said to Rebekah his mother, "Behold, Esau my brother is a hairy man and I am a smooth man. It may be that my father will feel me and discover that I am deceiving him; then I will bring a curse upon myself instead of a blessing." His mother replied, "Let your curse be upon me, my son; only do my

Isaac finished blessing Jacob

bidding, and go, bring the kids to me." So Jacob went and brought them to his mother; and she prepared savory meat of the kind that his father loved.

Then Rebekah took from her elder son Esau the best garments which were in the house, and put them on Jacob her younger son. And she put the skins of the kids upon his hands and upon the smooth part of his neck. She then put the savory meat and the bread, which she had prepared, into the hand of her son Jacob.

So Jacob went to his father and said, "My father." Isaac said, "Here I am; who are you, my son?" Jacob said to his father, "I am Esau your first-born son. I have done as you bade me; now sit up, I pray you, and eat of my venison, so that you may bless me." But Isaac said to his son, "How is it that you have found it so quickly, my son?" Jacob replied, "Because the Lord your God has brought it to me." Then Isaac said to Jacob, "Come near, I pray you, so that I may feel you, my son, to learn whether you are really my son Esau or not."

So Jacob went near to Isaac his father, who felt him and said, "The voice is Jacob's voice, but the hands are the hands of Esau." And he did not perceive that it was Jacob, because his hands were hairy like his brother Esau's hands; so he blessed him. Then Isaac said, "Are you really my son Esau?" Jacob replied, "I am." Then Isaac said, "Bring it to me and I will eat of your venison, so that I may bless you." So Jacob brought it to him, and he ate; and he brought him wine, and he drank. Then his father said to him, "Come near now and kiss me, my son." So Jacob came near and kissed him. And Isaac smelled his clothes, which were really Esau's, and bestowed his blessing upon Jacob, thinking that he was Esau.

As soon as Isaac had finished blessing Jacob, and when Jacob had scarcely gone out from the presence of his father, Esau his brother came in from his hunting. Esau had also prepared savory meat, and brought it now to his father. And Esau said to his father, "Let my father sit up, and eat of my venison, so that you may bless me." Isaac said to him, "Who are you?" Esau replied, "I am your son, your first-born son, Esau." Isaac trembled violently and said, "Who? Then who hunted for venison and brought it to me, and I ate of it before you came, and have blessed him? Yes, and he shall be blessed."

When Esau heard the words of his father, he cried out with an exceedingly great and bitter cry, and said to his father, "Bless me, even me also, O my father!" But Isaac said, "Your brother came with craft, and he has taken away your blessing." Esau said, "Is he not rightly named Jacob? For he has supplanted me these two times. He took away my birthright; and behold, now he has taken away my blessing. Have you not reserved a blessing for me?"

Isaac answered Esau, saying, "Behold, I have made Jacob your lord, and I have given him all his brothers for servants, and with grain and wine I have sustained him. What then shall I do for you, my son?" Esau said to his father, "Have you but one blessing, my father? Bless me, even me also, O my father." And Esau lifted up his voice and wept.

Now Esau hated Jacob for the way he had stolen his blessing, and Esau said to himself, "The days of mourning for my father are at hand; then I will kill my brother Jacob."

But these words of Esau her elder son were told to Rebekah. So she sent for Jacob her younger son and said to him, "Behold, your brother Esau consoles himself by preparing to kill you. Now therefore, my son, obey my voice; and arise, flee to Haran to Laban my brother, and stay with him for a while, until your brother's fury turns away from you and he forgets what you have done to him. Then I will send for you, and have you come back from Haran. Why should I lose both my sons in one day?"

Then Rebekah planned how to get Isaac to approve sending Jacob away. She pretended that she feared Jacob would marry one of the Hittite women, instead of a woman of their own people.

So Isaac called Jacob and blessed him, and charged him not to marry one of the Canaanite women. Thus Isaac sent Jacob away; and he went to Padan-aram to Laban, the son of Bethuel the Syrian, the brother of Rebekah, Jacob's and Esau's mother.

TWELVE

Jacob's Dream at Bethel

Genesis 28:6–29:14

WHEN Esau was forty years old, he married a Canaanite woman by the name of Judith, the daughter of Beeri; and another Canaanite woman by the name of Bashemath, the daughter of Elon. And we are told that Esau and his wives were a trial to Isaac and Rebekah.

Esau learned that his father Isaac had blessed Jacob and sent him away to Padan-aram to take a wife from there, and that he had charged Jacob not to marry one of the Canaanite women. Esau also knew that Jacob had obeyed his father and mother and had gone to Padan-aram. So when Esau realized that the Canaanite women did not please Isaac his father, he decided to take a wife from among his own people. He went to Ishmael, Abraham's son, and took as a wife, besides the wives he had, one of Ishmael's daughters. Her name was Mahalath, and she had a sister by the name of Nebajoth.

Meanwhile Jacob left his home at Beer-sheba and started on the long and lonely journey to Haran, more than four hundred miles away. When he reached a certain place in the hill country about ten miles north of Jerusalem, he decided to spend the night there, because the sun had set. Taking one of the many stones in the place, he used it for a pillow, and lay down there to sleep.

And Jacob had a wonderful dream that night. In his dream he saw a great ladder set up on the earth, the top of it reaching to heaven. And behold, the angels of God were ascending and descending on it! And behold, the Lord stood above it and said to Jacob, "I am the Lord God of Abraham your father, and the God of Isaac: I will give the land on which you are lying to you and to your descendants. And your descendants shall be like the dust of the earth, and you shall spread abroad to the west, and to the east, and to the north, and to the south: and through you and

Jacob told Rachel that he was her father's relative

your descendants shall all the families of the earth be blessed. Behold, I am with you, and will keep you wherever you go, and will bring you back to this land; for I will not leave you until I have done that of which I have spoken to you."

Then Jacob awoke from his sleep and said, "Surely the Lord is in this place; and I did not know it." And he was afraid and said, "How fearful is this place! This is none other but the house of God, and this is the gate of heaven."

So Jacob arose early in the morning, and took the stone which he had used for a pillow, and set it up as a pillar and poured oil on the top of it. And he called the name of that place Bethel, which means "house of God." The old Canaanite name for the town near Bethel was Luz. Then Jacob made a vow to the Lord, saying, "If God will be with me, and will keep me wherever I go, and will give me bread to eat and clothes to wear, so that I may come again to my father's house in peace, then the Lord shall be my God; and this stone, which I have set up as a pillar, shall be God's house; and of all that you shall give me I will surely give a tenth to you."

Then Jacob left Bethel and went on his journey, and came at last to the land of Padan-aram. He came to a well where a number of shepherds were gathered with their flocks of sheep. Jacob said to them, "My

brothers, where are you from?" They said, "We are from Haran." He said to them, "Do you know Laban the son of Nahor?" They replied, "Yes, we know him." Jacob inquired, "Is he well?" They said, "He is well; and behold, here comes his daughter Rachel with the sheep!"

While Jacob was still speaking with the shepherds, Rachel came with her father's sheep, for she kept them. Now when Jacob saw Rachel, the daughter of his mother's brother Laban, and when he saw the sheep of Laban, he went up and rolled the stone from the well's mouth, and watered the flock of Laban his uncle. Then Jacob kissed Rachel, and wept aloud. And Jacob told Rachel that he was her father's relative and that he was Rebekah's son. And Rachel ran and told her father.

When Laban heard that Jacob his sister's son was there, he ran out to meet him, and embraced him and kissed him, and brought him into his house. Jacob told Laban many things about his family in Beer-sheba, and how his parents had sent him to Haran to find a wife from among his own people. And Laban gave Jacob a warm welcome, saying, "Truly you are my bone and my flesh." And Jacob remained with Laban in Haran for what proved to be a very long and eventful period of his life.

THIRTEEN

Jacob Wrestles With the Angel

Genesis 32:1–33:20

JACOB continued to live with Laban in Haran for twenty years. He served Laban fourteen years so that he might marry his two daughters Leah and Rachel. He served six years longer for a share of Laban's flocks and herds. During this time eleven sons were born to Jacob by his two wives Leah and Rachel, and by their maids Zilpah and Bilhah. By hard work and clever planning, Jacob became rich and prosperous. He acquired large flocks of sheep and goats, great herds of cattle, and great numbers of camels and asses. He had a very large family, and numerous menservants and maidservants.

Seeing that Laban did not regard him with great favor any longer, Jacob decided to leave and go back to the land of Canaan. The Lord also said to Jacob, "Return to the land of your fathers, and to your family; and I will be with you." So Jacob gathered all his family together, and all his possessions, and fled from Haran without telling Laban that he was going. Laban was very angry when he learned this, and pursued Jacob. He caught up with him in the hill country of Gilead. After some heated arguments, the two settled their differences and made a solemn covenant by the pillar of Mizpah. The words of this covenant are as follows: "The Lord watch between you and me, when we are absent one from the other."

So Laban took leave of Jacob and went back to Haran. And Jacob continued his journey toward the land of Canaan.

As Jacob came to a certain place east of the Jordan, he began to fear what Esau might do to him when he returned to his old home. So Jacob sent messengers before him to Esau his brother in the country of Edom, ordering them to say to Esau, "Your servant Jacob says, 'I have sojourned with Laban and stayed there until now; and I have oxen, and asses, flocks, and menservants, and womenservants; and I have sent to tell my lord, in the hope that I may find favor in your sight once again.'"

And the messengers returned to Jacob, saying, "We came to your brother Esau, and behold, he is coming to meet you, and four hundred men with him." Then Jacob was greatly afraid and distressed; and he divided the people that were with him, and the flocks and herds and camels, into two companies, saying to himself, "If Esau comes to one company and attacks it, then the company which is left will escape."

Greatly fearing the vengeance of Esau for all the wrong he had done to him, Jacob turned to God in prayer and prayed earnestly that God would deliver him from the wrath of his brother Esau.

Then Jacob devised a wise plan by which he hoped to appease the wrath of Esau. He sent a large present ahead to Esau consisting of three separate droves of sheep and cattle. The servant in charge of each drove was to say to Esau, "They are your servant Jacob's, and are a present sent to my lord Esau; and be-

An angel of the Lord wrestled with Jacob

hold, he is coming behind us." So the present went on before him; and Jacob himself lodged in the camp that night.

That very night Jacob arose and took his two wives, his two maidservants, and his eleven children, and crossed the ford of the brook Jabbok. He took them and sent them and everything he had across the brook.

And in that midnight hour of peril and perplexity Jacob was left alone. He again sought guidance and strength in prayer. And an angel of the Lord wrestled with Jacob until the breaking of day. When the angel saw that he did not prevail against Jacob, he touched the hollow of his thigh; and the hollow of Jacob's thigh was put out of joint as he wrestled with him. Then the angel said, "Let me go, for day is breaking." But Jacob said, "I will not let you go unless you bless me."

And the angel said to him, "What is your name?" And he said, "Jacob." Then the angel said, "Your name shall no longer be Jacob, but Israel, for you have struggled with God and with men, and have prevailed." Then Jacob asked the angel, "Tell me, I pray, your name." The angel said, "Why do you ask my name?" And there the angel blessed Jacob.

So Jacob called that place Penuel, saying, "For I have seen God face to face, and my life is preserved." And as he passed Penuel the sun rose upon him, and he was limping because of his injured thigh.

And Jacob lifted up his eyes, and behold, Esau was coming, and with him four hundred men. So Jacob divided the children among Leah and Rachel and the two maidservants. And he put the maidservants with their children first, Leah with her children next, and Rachel and Joseph last. Jacob himself went ahead of them all, bowing himself to the ground seven times, until he came near to his brother.

And Esau, generous and forgiving, ran to meet Jacob, and embraced him, and kissed him, and they wept. And Jacob said to Esau, "Do take, I pray you, my gift that is brought to you, because God has dealt graciously with me, and because I have enough." Thus Jacob urged him, and Esau accepted the gift.

Then Esau proposed that they journey on together. But Jacob excused himself, saying that his children and cattle could not travel as fast as Esau would want to go. Then Esau suggested that he leave some of his men to accompany Jacob. But Jacob replied, "It is not necessary. Let me find favor in the sight of my lord."

So Esau returned that day on his way to Seir. And Jacob journeyed to Succoth, where he built himself a house and made stalls for his cattle. From there he went on safely to the city of Shechem, in the land of Canaan, where he pitched his tent and erected an altar to the God of Israel.

FOURTEEN

Joseph Is Sold Into Egypt

Genesis 37:1–36

JACOB continued to live in the land of Canaan, where his father had been a stranger. The years passed and Jacob's son Joseph grew to be a lad of seventeen. Rachel, the mother of Joseph, had died when she gave birth to Joseph's younger brother Benjamin. Joseph helped his older brothers—the sons of Leah, Bilhah, and Zilpah—take care of his father's flocks. One day Joseph brought an unfavorable report to Jacob concerning his brothers for a wrong they had done. Now Jacob loved Joseph more than any of his children, because he was the son of his old age; and he made him a coat of many colors. But when his brothers saw that their father loved Joseph more than all of them, they hated Joseph, and could not speak peaceably to him.

One time Joseph had a dream, and when he told his brothers about it they hated him all the more. This is what Joseph said to them: "Hear, I pray you, this dream which I have dreamed: for behold, we were binding sheaves in the field, and lo, my sheaf arose and stood upright; and behold, your sheaves stood round about and made obeisance to my sheaf."

His brothers angrily replied, "Will you indeed reign over us? Or will you indeed have dominion over us?" And they hated Joseph all the more for his dreams and for his words.

Soon Joseph had another dream and told it to his brothers, saying, "Behold, I have dreamed another dream; and behold, the sun, the moon, and the eleven stars made obeisance to me."

But when he told it to his father and to his brothers, his father rebuked him, saying, "What is this dream that you have dreamed? Shall I and your mother and your brothers indeed come to bow ourselves down to you and to the earth?" And his brothers were very jealous of him, but his father kept Joseph's words in mind.

Now Joseph's brothers went out to pasture their father's flock near Shechem, but Joseph remained at home. And Jacob called Joseph to him and said, "Your brothers are feeding the flock at Shechem. Go and see if it is well with your brothers, and with the flocks; and bring me word again." So Jacob sent Joseph from the valley of Hebron, and he came to Shechem. A certain man saw Joseph wandering about in the fields, and said to him, "What are you looking for?" Joseph replied, "I am looking for my brothers; tell me, I pray you, where they are feeding their flocks." And the man said, "They have gone from here, for I heard them say, 'Let us go to Dothan.'"

So Joseph went after his brothers, and finally found them at Dothan. When the brothers saw Joseph coming afar off, even before he came nearer, they conspired against him to kill him. They said to one another, "Look, here comes the dreamer. Come now, therefore, and let us kill him, and throw him into a pit; we will say some evil beast has devoured him, and we shall see what will become of his dreams."

When Reuben heard this wicked plot, he sought to deliver Joseph out of their hands. Reuben pleaded with his brothers, saying, "Let us not kill him. Let us shed no blood, but cast him into this pit that is in the wilderness and lay no hand upon him." What Reu-

ben had in mind was that he might later rescue Joseph from the pit and bring him back to his father. Reuben's counsel prevailed, and when Joseph came to his brothers, they stripped him of his coat, the coat of many colors that he wore; and they seized him and cast him into a deep pit. The pit was empty; there was no water in it.

Then the selfish brothers sat down to eat, not caring how Joseph suffered in the pit. Happening to look up, they beheld a caravan of Ishmaelite merchantmen coming from Gilead, bound for Egypt, with their camels bear-

Joseph's brothers sold him to the Ishmaelites for twenty pieces of silver

ing spices, balm, and myrrh. Judah said to his brothers, "What good is it to us if we kill our brother and conceal his blood? Come, let us sell him to the Ishmaelites, and let not our hand be upon him; for he is our brother, and our flesh." The brothers agreed to Judah's plan. Then, as the caravan of traders passed by, they pulled Joseph out of the pit and sold him to the Ishmaelites for twenty pieces of silver; and the merchants took Joseph with them to Egypt.

When Reuben returned from caring for the sheep to the pit where Joseph had been placed, and noticed that he was no longer in the pit, he tore his clothes in sorrow and dismay, and hurried back to his brothers. To them he exclaimed, "The lad is gone. Now what shall I do, where shall I go?"

The brothers took Joseph's coat, and killed a kid, and dipped the coat in the blood; then they brought the coat of many colors to their father, and said, "We have found this; see if you can tell whether it is your son's coat or not."

And Jacob recognized it and cried out, "It is my son's coat; an evil beast has devoured him; Joseph has without doubt been torn in pieces." Then the poor old father tore his clothes, and put sackcloth upon his loins, and mourned for Joseph many days. All his sons and all his daughters tried to comfort him, but he refused to be comforted, and said, "For I will go down to the grave to my son, mourning." Thus Jacob wept for Joseph, not knowing that some day he would see him again.

In the meantime the Ishmaelite merchants sold Joseph into Egypt to Potiphar, an officer of Pharaoh's, the captain of the guard.

FIFTEEN

Joseph Imprisoned in Egypt

Genesis 39:1–40:23

ALTHOUGH Joseph had been cruelly mistreated by his brothers, the Lord was with him and gave him success in Egypt in his service to Potiphar. As he served in the house of Potiphar, his Egyptian master saw that the Lord was with him and made all that he did prosper.

So Joseph found favor in Potiphar's sight, and served him, and Potiphar made him overseer of his house and of all that he had. From the time Joseph became overseer in Potiphar's house and over all that he had, the Lord blessed the Egyptian's house for Joseph's sake; and the blessing of the Lord was upon all that he had, in the house and in the field. So Potiphar left all that he had in Joseph's hands; and having such a faithful servant, Potiphar concerned himself with only the food which he ate.

Joseph was young and handsome. And after a while Potiphar's wife, who was a vain and foolish woman, cast her eyes upon Joseph

Joseph, although completely innocent, was kept in prison

with evil thoughts in her mind. But Joseph refused her unseemly advances, and said to his master's wife, "Behold, my master trusts me and has no concern for anything in the house, and he has left all that he has in my hands. There is no one greater in this house than I; nor has he kept back anything from me except you, because you are his wife. How then can I do this great wickedness, and sin against God?" And although she continued to make advances toward Joseph day after day, he would not pay her heed or be with her when it was not necessary.

However, one day, when Joseph went into the house to do his work, and none of the men of the house were there, his master's wife caught hold of his garment and tried to get him to make love to her. But Joseph pulled himself away, leaving his garment in her hand, and fled from the house. And when the wicked woman saw that Joseph had left his garment in her hand, and had fled from the house, she called her menservants and said to them, "See, my husband has brought us a Hebrew to insult us; he came in to make love to me, and I cried out; and when he heard me cry out with a loud voice, he left his garment with me and fled from the house."

When Potiphar came home that evening, she told him the same false story about Joseph. And she showed him the garment that Joseph had left behind when he ran out of the house. Potiphar, assuming that his wife was telling him the truth, became very angry at Joseph. Apparently Joseph was not given an opportunity to tell the truth about what had happened. At any rate, Potiphar took him and put him into the prison where the king's prisoners were confined; and Joseph, although completely innocent, was kept there.

But the God of his fathers continued to be with Joseph, and showed His loving-kindness by giving him favor in the sight of the keeper of the prison. Seeing that Joseph was an honest and trustworthy person, the keeper of the prison committed all of the prisoners to Joseph's care. Whatever was done in the prison, Joseph was the doer of it. The keeper of the prison did not bother with anything that was in Joseph's hands, because he saw that the Lord was with him. And whatever Joseph did in the management of prison affairs, the Lord made it prosper.

Some time afterward, two of Pharaoh's officers, the chief butler and the chief baker, offended the king of Egypt and were cast into the prison where Joseph was. One night both the chief butler and the chief baker had dreams which troubled them very much. They told their dreams to Joseph, and God gave him the wisdom to interpret them aright. For this kindness and favor, Joseph requested the chief butler to remember him when he got out of prison, and to intercede for him with Pharaoh so that he too might be brought out of prison. But when the chief butler was released from prison and restored to his butlership before Pharaoh, he forgot all about the promise he had made to Joseph. Thus Joseph continued to languish in the prison.

SIXTEEN

Joseph Is Made Ruler of Egypt

Genesis 41:1–57

AFTER Joseph had been in prison for two years, an event took place which, in the providence of God, was to change the whole future life of Joseph and his family. It had to do with Pharaoh's dream and the results of Joseph's interpretation of Pharaoh's dream.

In his dream Pharaoh was standing by the river Nile, and behold, there came up out of the river seven sleek fat cows, and they fed in the tall grass near by. And behold, seven other cows, thin and famished, came up after them out of the river, and stood by the other cows on the river bank. And the seven thin famished cows ate up the seven sleek fat cows. And Pharaoh awoke.

And Pharaoh fell asleep again and dreamed a second time; and behold, seven ears of good plump grain came up on one stalk. And behold, seven empty ears blighted by the east wind sprang up after them. And the seven thin ears swallowed up the seven plump and full ears. And Pharaoh awoke, and behold, it was a dream. But in the morning his spirit was troubled; and he sent for all the magicians of Egypt and all its wise men. And Pharaoh told them his dream, but none of them could interpret it to the king.

Then the chief butler addressed Pharaoh, saying, "I remember my faults this day." And he proceeded to tell Pharaoh how Joseph had rightly interpreted the dreams which he and the chief baker had dreamed in the prison.

Then Pharaoh sent for Joseph, and they brought him hastily out of the dungeon. After shaving himself and changing his clothes, Joseph came in to Pharaoh's presence. And Pharaoh said to Joseph, "I have had a dream, and none of my wise men can interpret it; and it has been reported to me that you can interpret dreams." Joseph humbly replied, "It is not in me; God shall give Pharaoh an answer of peace." Then Pharaoh related the twofold dream to Joseph.

When he had finished, Joseph said, "The dream of Pharaoh is really one; God has made known to Pharaoh what he is about to do. The seven good cows are seven years, and the seven good ears are seven years; the dream is one. The seven thin and famished cows that came up after them are seven years, and the seven empty ears blighted by the east wind are also seven years of famine. It is as I have said: God has revealed to Pharaoh what he is about to do. There will come seven years of great plenty throughout all the land of Egypt; but after them there will arise seven years of famine, and all the plenty will be forgotten in the land of Egypt. The famine will consume the land, and plenty will be unknown in the land by reason of that famine which shall follow, for it shall be very grievous."

Then Joseph counseled Pharaoh, saying, "Now therefore let Pharaoh choose a man discreet and wise, and set him over the land of Egypt. Let Pharaoh do this, and let him appoint officers over the land, and take up the fifth part of the crop of the land of Egypt in

Joseph stored away much grain during the seven years of plenty

the seven plenteous years. And let them gather all the food of those good years to come, and lay up grain under the authority of Pharaoh; and let them store it away in the cities as a reserve supply for the land of Egypt against the seven years of famine which are to come, so that the land may not perish as a result of the famine."

This advice seemed good to Pharaoh and to all his servants. And Pharaoh said to his servants, "Can we find such a man as Joseph, in whom is the Spirit of God?" Then Pharaoh said to Joseph, "Since God has shown all this to you, it is evident that there is none so discreet and wise as you are. Therefore I shall put you in charge of my house, and all my people shall be ruled by your command; only in regard to the throne will I be greater than you."

Then Pharaoh officially said to Joseph, "Behold, I have made you ruler over all the land of Egypt." And Pharaoh took his ring from his hand and put it on Joseph's hand, and arrayed him in robes of fine linen, and put a gold chain about his neck; and he made him ride in his second chariot; and they cried before him, "Bow the knee." Thus Pharaoh made Joseph a prince over all Egypt.

In addition Pharaoh said to Joseph, "I am Pharaoh, and without your approval no man shall lift up his hand or foot in all the land of Egypt." And Pharaoh called Joseph's name Zaphnath-paaneah, which means "The giver of the nourishment of life." And Pharaoh gave him in marriage Asenath, the daughter of Potipherah, priest of On.

Joseph was thirty years old when he began to serve the king of Egypt. He went out from the presence of Pharaoh, and went through all the land of Egypt. During the seven plenteous years the earth brought forth abundantly, and Joseph stored away in every city the food from the fields around it. And he stored away so much grain that he stopped keeping a record of it, for it was like the sand of the sea and could not be measured.

Before the years of famine came, Asenath bore Joseph two sons. Joseph called the firstborn Manasseh, meaning, "making to forget." "For God," he said, "has made me forget all my toil and hardship, and all my father's house." He called the second Ephraim, "For God has caused me to be fruitful in the land of my affliction."

The seven years of plenty in the land of Egypt came to an end; and the seven years of famine began, just as Joseph had said. There was famine everywhere; but in the land of Egypt there was bread. When all the land of Egypt was famished, the people cried to Pharaoh for bread; and Pharaoh said to all the Egyptians, "Go to Joseph; and what he says, you must do." Thus, when the famine had spread throughout the land, Joseph opened all the storehouses and sold grain to the Egyptians, for the famine was severe in the land of Egypt. People from other countries came to Egypt to Joseph to buy grain, because the famine was severe in their lands also. Thus Joseph's wise plan of food conservation saved the lives of thousands of people.

SEVENTEEN

Joseph Makes Himself Known to His Brothers

Genesis 42:1–45:28

WHEN Jacob heard that there was an abundance of grain in Egypt, he sent ten of his sons down to Egypt to buy grain to keep his family alive. But Jacob did not send Joseph's younger brother Benjamin, because he was afraid that some harm might befall him. Thus the sons of Jacob were among the others who came from the land of Canaan to buy grain.

Now Joseph was governor over Egypt, and it was he who sold food to all the people of the land. And behold, Joseph's brothers came and bowed down before him. Joseph recognized his brothers, but they did not recognize him. So to test them, Joseph treated them as strangers and spoke roughly to them. As they bowed down before him, he remembered the dreams which he had dreamed of them. These dreams were now coming true.

Joseph pretended to accuse them of being spies who had come to see the barrenness of the land. But they said they were all the sons of one man, honest men, and that they had come only to buy food. Joseph insisted that they were spies, and put them all in prison for three days.

On the third day, Joseph said he would keep one of the brothers in prison, and let the rest go and carry grain back to their hungry households. He made them promise that they would bring their youngest brother Benjamin to him when they returned to Egypt. The brothers began to be conscience-stricken for the wrong they had done to Joseph, and to realize that now the day of reckoning was upon them. Joseph understood their conversation, and he turned away from them and wept unseen. Then Joseph took Simeon from them and held him as a hostage. And Joseph gave instructions that their bags be filled with grain, and that each man's money be restored in his sack, and that they be given provisions for the journey back to Canaan. This was done.

On the return journey, one of the men opened his sack and was surprised to find his money in the mouth of it. At this discovery, all the brothers were greatly afraid, and said to one another, "What is this that God has done to us?"

When they came to their father Jacob in Canaan, they told him all that had befallen them in Egypt. And as they emptied the grain out of their sacks, behold, each man's money was in his sack, and they were all greatly dismayed. Then Jacob said to them, "You have bereaved me of my children: Joseph is gone, and Simeon is gone, and now you would take Benjamin away from me." And he lamented concerning all the troubles that had come upon him.

The famine continued to be severe in Canaan, and before long the grain which the brothers had brought from Egypt was all eaten up. Then Jacob said to his sons, "Go again into Egypt and buy us a little food." But they said that there was no use going unless they took Benjamin with them. Jacob was very reluctant to give his consent, until Judah earnestly declared that he would be surety for Benjamin.

Finally their father Jacob said to them, "If it must be so now, do this: take some of the choicest fruits of the land in your sacks, and carry down to the man a present, a little balm and a little honey, spices, myrrh, nuts, and almonds. Take a double amount of money with you; take back the money that was returned in the mouth of your sacks; it may have been an oversight. Take also your brother Benjamin, and arise, go again to the man; and may God Almighty grant you mercy before him, so that he may send back your other brother and Benjamin. If I am bereaved of my children, I am bereaved." So the men took with them the present, and a double amount of money, and Benjamin; and they arose and went down to Egypt, and stood before Joseph a second time.

When Joseph saw that his brothers had kept their word and had brought Benjamin with them, he commanded his steward to arrange for their entertainment in his own house. He received the present they had brought, and saw to it that they were served with plenty of food. He inquired after their welfare, and asked, "Is your father well, the old man of whom you spoke? Is he still alive?" They replied, "Your servant our father is in good health; he is still alive." Joseph saw to it that Benjamin's share was five times as much as any of the others. So they ate and drank and had a merry time with Joseph.

But Joseph decided to test them further. So he commanded his steward to fill their sacks with food, and put each man's money in his sack, and to conceal his silver cup in Benjamin's. Then early in the morning he sent them on their way.

And when they were not yet far off, he sent his steward after them. The steward quickly overtook them, and accused them of stealing his master's silver cup. The brothers of course denied that they had done such a thing. But every man was ordered to search his sack, and the silver cup was found in Benjamin's.

They were taken back in shame and fear to Joseph's house. Joseph said he would let the others go but that he must keep Benjamin as his servant. Whereupon Judah made a noble plea and entreaty on Benjamin's behalf that he be restored to his old father.

Then Joseph could not restrain himself any longer, and he wept aloud, and sent all of his Egyptian servants out of the room. So no one stayed with Joseph while he made himself known to his brothers. And Joseph said to them, "I am Joseph. Is my father still alive?" But his brothers could not answer him, for they were greatly dismayed and troubled by his disclosure.

So Joseph said to his brothers, "I am your brother Joseph, whom you sold into Egypt. But do not be grieved or angry with yourselves for selling me here; for it was God's will to send me before you to preserve life." Then he bade them to make haste and go up to his father and say to him, "Thus says your son Joseph: 'God has made me lord of all Egypt; do not delay to come down to me. You shall live in the land of Goshen, and you shall be near me, you, and your children, and your

Joseph made himself known to his brothers

children's children, and your flocks, your herds, and all that you have. There I will take care of you, for there yet remain five years of famine; lest you and your household, and all that you have, come to poverty.'"

Then he fell upon his brother Benjamin's neck and wept; and Benjamin wept upon his neck. And he kissed all his brothers and wept upon them; and after that his brothers talked with him.

Pharaoh was pleased to hear that Joseph's brothers had come, and that Joseph had made himself known to them. He urged Joseph to send his brothers back with a generous supply of food, and to have them bring their father and their households and come to dwell in Egypt. Pharaoh offered them wagons to transport their goods, and promised to give them the best of the land of Egypt to settle in.

The sons of Jacob did as they were bidden; and Joseph gave them wagons and provisions for the journey. To each of them he gave changes of raiment; but to Benjamin he gave three hundred pieces of silver and five changes of raiment. He sent a large present of grain, bread, and food to his father; and said to his brothers as they were going, "See that you do not quarrel with one another along the way."

So when the brothers came back to their father Jacob, they said to him, "Joseph is still alive, and he is governor over all the land of Egypt." This was hard for Jacob to believe, and his heart almost failed him. But when they told him all the words of Joseph, and when he saw the wagons which Joseph had sent to carry him, the spirit of Jacob revived. And Jacob said, "It is enough; Joseph my son is still alive; I will go and see him before I die."

EIGHTEEN

Joseph Receives His Father Jacob in Egypt

Genesis 46:1–50:26

HAVING heard the good news that his son Joseph was alive, Jacob journeyed with all that he had to Beer-sheba, and there offered sacrifices to the God of his father Isaac. And God spoke to Jacob in visions of the night, saying, "Jacob, Jacob." And he said, "Here am I." Then the Lord said, "I am God, the God of your father; do not be afraid to go down into Egypt; for I will make of you there a great nation. I will go down with you into Egypt; and I will also surely bring you up again; and Joseph shall put his hand upon your eyes."

Then Jacob went forth from Beer-sheba; and his sons carried Jacob their father, their little ones, and their wives in the wagons which Pharaoh had sent. They also took their cattle and their goods, which they had gathered in the land of Canaan, and came into Egypt, Jacob and all his family, and all his possessions. And the number of persons belonging to Jacob who came to Egypt was seventy.

Jacob sent his son Judah before him to appear before Joseph in the land of Goshen. Then Joseph made ready his chariot and went up to meet Jacob his father in Goshen. And Joseph presented himself to Jacob, and fell on his neck, and wept on his neck a good while. Then Jacob said to Joseph, "Now let me die, now that I have seen your face and know that you are still alive."

Then Joseph went and told Pharaoh, "My father and my brothers, and their flocks and their herds, and all that they have, are come out of the land of Canaan; and behold, they are now in the land of Goshen." And Joseph took five of his brothers and presented them to Pharaoh. The king of Egypt said to Joseph's brothers, "What is your occupation?" And they replied, "Your servants are shepherds, we, and our fathers, and their fathers before them." They also said to Pharaoh, "We have come to the land to sojourn here; for your

Joseph presented himself to Jacob

servants have no pasture for their flocks, the famine being very severe in the land of Canaan. And now, we pray you, let your servants settle in the land of Goshen." Then Pharaoh said to Joseph, "The land of Egypt is before you; give your father and your brothers the best of the land; let them settle in the land of Goshen; and if you know any capable men among them, make them overseers of my cattle."

Then Joseph brought his father Jacob before Pharaoh, and Jacob blessed Pharaoh. The king asked Jacob how old he was, and Jacob said that he was a hundred and thirty years old. And Jacob blessed Pharaoh again, and went out from before him.

Thus Jacob and his family settled in the land of Goshen; and they gathered possessions there, and grew and multiplied exceedingly. And Jacob lived in the land of Egypt seventeen years; so Jacob's age came to a hundred and forty-seven years.

And when the time drew near for Jacob to die, he called Joseph to him and said, "If now I have found favor in your sight, put your hand under my thigh and promise to deal kindly and truly with me. Do not bury me, I pray you, in Egypt, but let me lie with my fathers; carry me out of Egypt and bury me where they are buried." Joseph replied, "I will do as you have said." And Jacob said, "Swear to me"; and Joseph swore to him. Then Jacob bowed himself upon the head of the bed.

Before he died, Jacob called his sons before him and pronounced a blessing upon them, with a suitable blessing for each one. Then he said, "I am to be gathered to my people; bury me with my fathers in the cave that is in the field of Machpelah, in the land of Canaan, which Abraham bought as a burying place." When Jacob finished giving his sons

instructions, he drew his feet up into the bed, and breathed his last, and was gathered to his people.

Then Joseph fell on his father's face, and wept over him, and kissed him. And Joseph commanded his servants the physicians to embalm his father. So the physicians embalmed Jacob; forty days were necessary for embalming, according to the custom of the Egyptians. And the Egyptians mourned for Jacob seventy days.

After the days of mourning for Jacob were past, Joseph and his brothers carried their father back to the land of Canaan, and buried him in the field of Machpelah as Jacob had commanded them. After he had buried his father, Joseph returned to Egypt with his brothers and all who had gone with him to bury his father.

When Joseph's brothers saw that their father was dead, they said, "It may be that Joseph will hate us and take revenge upon us for all the evils which we did to him." So they sent a message to Joseph, saying, "Your father gave this command before he died, 'Say to Joseph, "Forgive, I pray you, your brothers' transgression and their sin, for they did you evil." ' And now, we pray you, forgive the transgression of the servants of the God of your father."

Joseph wept when they spoke to him thus. His brothers also came and fell down before him and said, "Behold, we are your servants." And Joseph said to them, "Fear not, for am I in the place of God? As for you, you meant evil against me; but God meant it for good, to bring it about that many people should be saved, even as they are today. So do not be afraid; I will take care of you and your little ones." Thus Joseph reassured his brothers.

So Joseph dwelt in Egypt, he and his father's house; and Joseph lived a hundred and ten years. And Joseph said to his brothers, "I am dying; but God will surely visit you, and bring you up out of this land to the land which he promised to Abraham, to Isaac, and to Jacob." Then Joseph took an oath of the sons of Jacob, saying, "God will surely visit you, and you shall carry up my bones from here." So Joseph died, being a hundred and ten years old; and they embalmed him, and he was put in a coffin in Egypt.

II.

STORIES

ABOUT MOSES

AND THE

ISRAELITES

NINETEEN

The Baby Moses and His Strange Cradle

Exodus 1:1–2:10

WHEN Jacob and his family went to sojourn in Goshen in the land of Egypt they were seventy in number. The Israelites continued to live in Egypt for over four hundred years, and the descendants of Jacob increased and multiplied until they became a very great people. They spread out over the country until the land was filled with them.

Now there arose a new king over Egypt, who did not know Joseph and what he had done for Egypt in years gone by. This new Pharaoh had a very hostile feeling toward the Israelites. He saw how rapidly the Israelites were increasing, and he feared that if war came the Israelites would join their enemies and fight against Egypt, and try to escape from the land. So the king and his officers decided to make the Israelites work harder, thinking that this would make them weaker and less dangerous. They set taskmasters over them to afflict them with heavy burdens, and put them to work building cities to contain the treasures of Pharaoh.

But the more the Israelites were oppressed, the more they grew and multiplied. And the Egyptians feared the strength of the Israelites more than ever. They made the Israelites serve more and more rigorously, and made their lives bitter with hard labor, in mortar and brick, and in all manner of work in the field.

Then the king thought of another plan to stop the increase of the Israelites. He ordered the midwives of the Hebrew women to put to death every male child who should be born, but to allow the female babies to live. But the midwives feared God, and did not carry out the king's commandment. Then Pharaoh in anger ordered all his people to obey this edict: "Every son that is born to the Hebrews you shall cast into the Nile, but every daughter you shall allow to live." This wicked decree caused great dismay and distress among the Israelites.

At this time a certain man from the family of Levi took as his wife a daughter of Levi. In due time the woman gave birth to a child, a very beautiful baby boy. When the mother saw what a handsome child he was, she kept him hidden in her home for three months. Her faith in God gave her courage to disobey the king's edict, and wisdom to find the right way to save the life of her child.

When the child became three months old, and began to cry loud enough for people outside the house to hear, the mother realized that she could not hide him thus any longer. So she carefully made a basket, woven from the bulrushes which grew along the river bank, and sealed it with mud and pitch to keep the water out. She lined the basket with soft material, tucked the little child in it, and placed it with its precious burden among the tall grasses at the river's brink. Then, surmising what would happen, she had her daughter Miriam stand near by to watch over the baby and see what would be done to him.

Presently, according to her custom, the

67

The princess was amazed to see a beautiful baby boy

daughter of Pharaoh, princess of Egypt, came down to wash herself at the river, and her maidens walked along by the river's edge. Suddenly the princess saw the basket among the reeds and sent one of her maids to bring it to her. When Pharaoh's daughter opened the covering of the basket, she was amazed to see a beautiful baby boy! The baby was crying, and the heart of the princess was immediately touched. She said to her maidens, who quickly gathered around to see, "This is one of the Hebrews' children." She evidently did not agree with her father's cruel edict that all Hebrew baby boys should be drowned in the Nile.

At this precise moment, Miriam, the baby's sister, ran forward and said to Pharaoh's daughter, "Shall I go and bring you a nurse from the Hebrew women to nurse the child for you?" Pharaoh's daughter thought that was a very good suggestion, and she said to the little girl, "Go and do that very thing." So Miriam ran as fast as she could and called her own mother, and brought her to the scene. Pharaoh's daughter said to the child's mother, "Take this child away and nurse him for me, and I will give you wages for it." So the mother took her beautiful baby boy home again and nursed him for many months to come. Imagine how happy the mother was to have the privilege of thus caring for her own son; and now without dread of the king's commandment!

The child grew with the passing years, and when the proper time came the mother brought the boy to Pharaoh's daughter, who adopted him as her son. Then Pharaoh's daughter named the boy Moses, which means "drawn out"; for she said, "Because I drew him out of the water." As the adopted son of Pharaoh's daughter, Moses grew up in the court life of Egypt and was instructed in all the learning and wisdom of the Egyptians. He grew up to be a strong and noble young man, and was mighty in his words and deeds.

TWENTY

Moses' Call of God at the Burning Bush

Exodus 3:1–4:31

MOSES was forty years old when he left behind forever the court life of Egypt and went to live in the land of Midian. He remained in Midian for forty years, caring for the flocks of Jethro, who became his father-in-law. These forty years were years of preparation for Moses' future work. Living the life of a shepherd, he learned to know all about the wilderness: its roads, its resources, its climate, and the mode of life of the people who lived there. He had much time for study and reflection upon the truths of religion and the works of God.

At the close of this period, Moses received a remarkable revelation from God. One day, as usual, Moses was keeping the flock of his father-in-law Jethro, the priest of Midian; he led his flock to the west side of the desert and came to Horeb, called the mountain of God. And suddenly the angel of the Lord appeared to Moses in a flame of fire out of the middle of a bush; and as Moses looked, behold, the bush was burning but it was not consumed. Moses was fascinated and said, "I will now turn aside and see this great sight, why the bush is not burned."

When the Lord saw that Moses turned aside to see, God called to him out of the bush and said, "Moses, Moses." And Moses said, "Here am I." Then the Lord said, "Do not draw near; but take off your shoes, for the place on which you are standing is holy ground." And the Lord said, "I am the God of your father, the God of Abraham, the God of Isaac, and the God of Jacob." And Moses hid his face in his arms, for he was afraid to look at God.

Then the Lord told Moses that He had seen the affliction of His people in Egypt, and that He knew their trials and sufferings. He promised Moses that He would deliver the Israelites out of the hand of the Egyptians and bring them to a good land, a land flowing with milk and honey, to the land inhabited by the Canaanites, the Hittites, the Amorites, the Perizzites, the Hivites, and the Jebusites. The Lord said to Moses, "Come, therefore, and I will send you to Pharaoh so that you may bring forth my people, the children of Israel, out of Egypt." But Moses said to God, "Who am I that I should go to Pharaoh and bring forth the children of Israel out of Egypt?" The Lord assured Moses, saying, "I will go with you; and this shall be a sign to you that I have sent you: when you have brought forth the people out of Egypt you shall serve God upon this mountain."

But Moses was still doubtful and reluctant. So he asked the Lord, "When I come to the people of Israel and say to them, 'The God of your fathers has sent me to you,' and they say to me, 'What is his name?' what shall I tell them?" And God said to Moses, "I AM WHO I AM." The Lord also said to Moses, "Tell this to the people of Israel, 'I AM has sent me to you.'" Then God instructed Moses to go and gather the elders of Israel together and tell them what the Lord had promised to do.

Since Moses was still doubtful that the elders and people would believe his word, God further assured him by showing signs and wonders. The Lord said to Moses, "What do you have in your hand?" Moses said, "A rod." And the Lord said, "Throw it on the ground." Moses did so and it became a serpent; and Moses fled from it. Then the Lord told Moses to take the serpent by the tail; and when he did so it became a rod in his hand again. Then the Lord said to Moses, "Now put your hand into your bosom." Moses did this; and when he took it out, behold, his hand was leprous, as white as snow. Then God said, "Put your hand into your bosom again." Moses obeyed; and when he took it out, behold, it had become again like the rest of his flesh. God told Moses that by these signs the people would believe that the God of their fathers had appeared to Moses and commissioned him to lead them out of Egypt.

But Moses had another excuse. He said, "Oh, my Lord, I am not eloquent; I am slow of speech and of tongue." Then the Lord said to Moses, "Who has created man's mouth? Who makes a man dumb, or deaf, or seeing, or blind? Is it not I, the Lord? Now therefore go, and I will be with your mouth and teach you what you shall say." But still Moses remonstrated, saying, "Oh, my Lord, send, I pray you, someone else."

Then the anger of the Lord was kindled against Moses and he said, "Is not Aaron the

The angel of the Lord appeared to Moses in a flame of fire out of the middle of a bush

Levite your brother? I know that he can speak well; and behold, he is coming forth to meet you, and when he sees you he will be glad in his heart. And you shall speak to Aaron, and he shall be your spokesman to the people. He shall be as a mouth for you, and you shall be to him as God. And you shall take this rod in your hand, for with it you shall perform signs."

Then Moses went back to Jethro, and asked permission to return to Egypt to visit his people. And Jethro said to Moses, "Go in peace." And the Lord said to Moses in Midian, "Go, return to Egypt; for all the men are dead who were trying to take your life." So Moses took his wife and his two sons, and returned to the land of Egypt; and Moses took the rod of God into his very own hand.

The Lord said to Aaron, "Go into the wilderness to meet Moses." So Aaron went, and met his brother at Mount Horeb and kissed him. And Moses related to Aaron all that the Lord had said to him, and about all the signs which the Lord had commanded him to perform. Then Moses and Aaron went and gathered together all the elders of the children of Israel. And Aaron repeated all the words which the Lord had spoken to Moses, and performed the signs in the sight of the people. And the people believed; and when they heard that the Lord had visited the children of Israel and that he had seen their affliction, they bowed their heads and worshiped the God of their fathers.

TWENTY-ONE

Moses and the Ten Plagues

Exodus 7:1–10:29

PHARAOH, the king of Egypt, continued to oppress and afflict the Israelites more and more severely. But God promised His servant Moses that the day of deliverance was near at hand. God instructed Moses and Aaron to go and stand before Pharaoh, and to demand of him, in the name of the Lord, that he let the people of Israel go out of his land. But the Lord told Moses that Pharaoh's heart would be hardened, and that he would at first refuse to let the people go. Therefore, God said, He would bring great acts of judgment and punishment upon Egypt, by the hand of Moses and

Aaron, until Pharaoh at last came to terms. These great acts of judgment are known as the Ten Plagues of Egypt.

The first was the plague of blood. Moses met Pharaoh by the bank of the river Nile, and said to him, "Thus says the Lord: 'By this you shall know that I am the Lord: behold, I will strike the waters that are in the river Nile with the rod that is in my hand, and they shall be turned to blood, and the fish in the river shall die, and the waters shall become polluted, and the Egyptians will loathe to drink water from the river.'" Moses and Aaron did as the Lord commanded, and the river was turned to blood. But Pharaoh's heart remained hardened, and he would not let the people go.

The second plague was the plague of frogs. Moses and Aaron, in obedience to God's command, stretched out their rod over the waters of Egypt, and a plague of frogs swarmed over the country, coming into the houses of the people; into their bedchambers and beds; into their ovens and kneading troughs, and everywhere. Then Pharaoh called Moses and Aaron, and said, "Entreat the Lord to take away the frogs from me and my people; and I will let your people go so that they may sacrifice to the Lord." But Pharaoh did not keep his word. When the plague of frogs was removed, he still would not let the people go.

The third act of judgment was the plague of lice. The Lord said to Moses, "Stretch out your rod and strike the dust of the earth, so that it may become lice throughout all the land of Egypt." When this was done, there came great numbers of lice on man and beast throughout all the land of Egypt. But still Pharaoh would not listen to Moses and Aaron, even as the Lord had said.

The fourth plague was the sending of swarms of flies into the houses of the Egyptians and upon all their people. But the plague of flies did not come upon the Israelites in the land of Goshen. This time Pharaoh said he would let the people go three days' journey into the wilderness to sacrifice to the Lord if the plague were removed. Moses prayed to the Lord, and the Lord removed the swarm of flies from Pharaoh and his people. But Pharaoh hardened his heart this time also, and did not let the people go.

The fifth plague fell upon the cattle of Egypt. Moses spoke to Pharaoh in the name of the Lord, saying, "The hand of the Lord will fall upon your cattle which are in the fields, upon the horses, the asses, the camels, the oxen, and the sheep; and there shall be a very severe plague of murrain." And on the next day the Lord did this thing; all the cattle of the Egyptians died, but of the cattle of the Israelites not one died. But Pharaoh still stubbornly refused to let the people go.

The sixth plague came upon the Egyptians in the form of boils. The Lord said to Moses and Aaron, "Take handfuls of ashes from the furnace, and let Moses throw them toward heaven in the sight of Pharaoh. And it shall fall as fine dust over all the land of Egypt, and shall become a plague of boils breaking out in sores on man and beast throughout all the land of Egypt." This came to pass as the Lord had said, and great was the suffering of man and beast from these sores. But Pharaoh was not yet ready to listen to the word of Moses and Aaron.

The seventh plague was a severe hailstorm upon the land of Egypt. The Lord directed Moses to say to Pharaoh, "You continue to exalt yourself against my people, and will not let them go." And the Lord said to Moses, "Stretch forth your hand toward heaven, so that there may be hail in all the land of Egypt, upon man and upon beast, and upon every plant in the fields, throughout the land of Egypt." Then Moses did as he was commanded, and the Lord rained hail and fire upon the land of Egypt. There was very heavy hail, and fire mingled with the hail, such as had not been seen in all the land of Egypt since it had become a nation. The hail struck throughout all the land of Egypt, and slashed down everything that was in the fields, both man and beast; and the hail slashed every plant of the field, and destroyed every tree of the field. Only in the land of Goshen, where the Israelites lived, was there no hail. Again

The Lord rained hail and fire upon the land of Egypt

Pharaoh showed signs of repentance, and made other false promises. But when the hailstorm ceased, by Moses' entreaty of the Lord, Pharaoh forgot his promises and refused to let the people go.

The eighth plague visited upon Pharaoh and his people was the plague of locusts. Moses and Aaron again appealed to Pharaoh to let their people go, but they were driven from Pharaoh's presence. Then the Lord said to Moses, "Stretch out your hand over the land of Egypt so that the locusts may come, and eat every plant in the land of Egypt that the hail has left." Moses obeyed; and a dense swarm of locusts, greater than there had ever been before, settled over the whole land of Egypt. They covered the face of the whole country, so that it was darkened, and they ate all the plants and all the fruit of the trees which the hail had left, until there remained not one green thing in the trees, or in the plants of the field, through all the land of Egypt.

The ninth plague brought a thick darkness over the land of Egypt. The Lord said to Moses, "Stretch out your hand toward heaven, so that there may be darkness over the land of Egypt, a darkness which may even be felt." So Moses obeyed the voice of the Lord, and stretched forth his hand toward heaven. Then there came a thick darkness over all the land of Egypt for a space of three days. The people of Egypt did not see one another, nor did anyone get up from where he was for three days. But during this blackout, all the children of Israel had light in their dwellings. Then Pharaoh called Moses and said, "Go forth now, and serve the Lord; take your children with you; but you must leave your flocks and herds behind." But Moses would not agree to this; for he told Pharaoh that they had to have their cattle in order to serve the Lord and offer sacrifices to him. So again Pharaoh's heart was hardened, and he would not let them go. Then Pharaoh said to Moses, "Go away from me; be careful that you do not see my face again; for on the day that you see my face you shall die." Without fear, Moses replied to Pharaoh, "You have spoken well. I will not see your face again."

TWENTY-TWO

Moses Institutes the Passover

Exodus 11:1–12:36

THE Lord said to Moses that He would send one more plague upon Pharaoh and upon Egypt, and that afterward Pharaoh would be entirely willing to let the people of Israel go. This tenth and last plague was the severest of all; for it meant the death of the oldest child in every Egyptian home. The Lord spoke thus to Moses: "About midnight I will go out into the midst of Egypt; and all the first-born in the land of Egypt shall die, from the first-born of Pharaoh who sits on his throne even to the first-born of the maidservant who is behind the mill, and all the first-born of the cattle. And there shall be a great cry throughout all the land of Egypt, such as was never heard before and never shall again."

Then God told Moses what he must do in order to have the death angel pass over the houses of the Israelites; and what the people must do in order to be ready to march out of Egypt. Moses instructed the people to prepare and eat the passover feast as a memorial of their deliverance from the death angel and from Egyptian bondage.

On the fourteenth day of the first month of their new year, each family was to take a male lamb without blemish, a year old, and prepare it for the passover feast. They were to take some of the blood of the slain lamb and sprinkle it on the two side posts and on the upper post of the doors of the houses in which the lambs were eaten. They were to roast the lamb and eat the flesh that night, together with unleavened bread and bitter herbs. Also they were to eat the feast with their loins girded, their shoes on their feet, and their staffs in their hands, ready to march in haste.

For the Lord said, "It is the Lord's passover. For I will pass through the land of Egypt that night, and will slay all the first-born in the land of Egypt, both man and beast. And the blood shall be a sign for you upon your houses; and when I see the blood, I will pass over you, and the plague shall not be upon you to destroy you when I strike the land of Egypt."

Moses assembled all the elders of Israel and directed them how to carry out the Lord's commandment, and instructed them concerning the meaning of this important event. Moses said to them further, "And you shall observe this service as an ordinance for you and for your sons forever. And it shall come to pass, when you come to the land which the Lord will give you according to his promise, that you shall keep this service. And it shall come to pass, when your children say to you, 'What do you mean by this service?' that you shall say, 'It is the sacrifice of the Lord's passover, who passed over the houses of the children of Israel in Egypt when He slew the Egyptians and spared our houses.' " When the people heard this they bowed their heads and worshiped God.

At midnight the Lord slew all the first-born

There was a great cry of lamentation in Egypt

in the land of Egypt, from the first-born of Pharaoh who sat on his throne to the first-born of the captive who was in the dungeon, and all the first-born of the cattle. And Pharaoh rose up in the night, and all his servants, and all the Egyptians; and there was a great cry of lamentation in Egypt, for there was not a house where there was not one dead. And Pharaoh summoned Moses and Aaron by night, and said to them, "Rise up, and set you forth from among my people, both you and the children of Israel; and go, serve the Lord, as you have said. Also take your flocks and your herds, as you have said, and be gone; and bless me also."

And the Egyptians urgently entreated the Israelites to leave their land in haste; for they said, "We will all be dead." So the children of Israel took their dough before it was leavened, and their kneading troughs bound up in their cloaks upon their shoulders. They also did as Moses had bidden them and asked to borrow jewels of silver and jewels of gold, and clothing, from the Egyptians. The Lord gave the people favor in the sight of the Egyptians, so that they lent those things that they requested. Thus, on that memorable night of the passover, the children of Israel ended their long sojourn and period of servitude in the land of Egypt.

TWENTY-THREE

Moses Leads the Israelites Out of Egypt

Exodus 12:37–13:22

AND so the mighty exodus of the children of Israel from the land of Egypt took place. The first stage of the journey was from Rameses in Goshen to Succoth near the Red Sea. About six hundred thousand men on foot, besides women and children, made up the vast company of pilgrims. It is estimated that the huge throng numbered close to three million souls. They also took with them their numerous flocks of sheep and herds of cattle. The women baked unleavened bread with the dough they had brought out of Egypt, because they had left in such haste that they did not have time to prepare other provisions.

The period of time that the children of Israel had been in Egypt, since Jacob and his family went to sojourn there, was four hundred and thirty years. It was at the end of this long stay that all the hosts of the Lord went out from the land of Egypt. Therefore it has been observed as a night of watching, sacred to the Lord, by the children of Israel through all their generations.

Then Moses instructed the people to observe the passover as an ordinance once a year, and keep the feast of unleavened bread for a period of seven days in connection with the passover feast. They were to teach their children what the passover meant, so that they might remember how the hand of the Lord had brought them out of Egypt.

Moses led the children of Israel from the land of Egypt

Moses also commanded the people to sanctify their first-born children to the Lord to help them remember how the Israelites had been spared when the first-born of the Egyptians had been slain. They were also to sanctify the firstlings of their cattle as offerings to the Lord in gratitude for God's great deliverance of His people.

This is the way Moses talked to the people: "When the Lord brings you into the land of the Canaanites, which He promised to your fathers, and gives it to you, you shall set apart to the Lord every first-born child. All the first-born of your cattle that are males shall be the Lord's too. And when in the future your son asks you, 'What does this mean?' you shall say to him, 'By strength of hand the Lord brought us out from Egypt, from the house of bondage. For when Pharaoh steadfastly refused to let us go, the Lord slew all the first-born in the land of Egypt, both the first-born of man and the first-born of beast. It shall be as a sign on your hand and as frontlets between your eyes; for by a mighty hand the Lord brought us out of Egypt.' "

When Pharaoh let the people go out of Egypt, they still needed God's protecting care and guidance. So God did not lead them by way of the land of the Philistines, although that was the most direct route to Canaan. For God said, "If they have to make war against the Philistines, they may change their minds and want to return to Egypt." But God led the Hebrew people about by way of the wilderness and the Red Sea. This would give them the opportunity to become better organized and better adapted to the life of struggle and discipline which would make them a strong nation. Even so they were not a helpless people, for they went forth out of the land of Egypt equipped for war.

At the time of the exodus, Joseph had been dead for about three hundred years; his embalmed body had rested all that time in Egypt. So Moses took the remains of Joseph in a coffin with him; for Joseph, before he died, had strictly sworn the children of Israel, saying, "God will surely visit you; and you shall carry up my bones from here." This sacred promise was fulfilled, and Joseph was eventually buried at Shechem, in the portion of ground which his father Jacob had purchased, in the very center of the Promised Land.

And the Israelites continued on their way from Succoth, and encamped at Etham, at the edge of the wilderness. And the presence of the Lord went before them by day in a pillar of cloud to show them the way, and by night in a pillar of fire to give them light, so that they could travel both by day and by night. And God did not take away the pillar of cloud by day or the pillar of fire by night from before the people. Thus the people knew that God was with them, and they were comforted and strengthened by His presence.

TWENTY-FOUR

Moses and the Israelites Cross the Red Sea

Exodus 14:1–15:2

FROM their first encampment at Etham, the Lord directed Moses to lead the people to the shore of the Red Sea, where they encamped at a place called Pi-hahiroth, between Migdol and the sea. The Lord informed Moses that Pharaoh would quickly regret that he had let the Israelites go, and that he would pursue them and try to destroy them. But the Lord assured his servant Moses that Pharaoh's evil intention would come to naught.

When the king of Egypt was told that the Israelites had fled, he did change his mind toward them, and said, "Why have we done this, why have we let Israel go from serving us?" So he made ready his chariot and took his army with him, and took six hundred picked chariots and all the other chariots of Egypt with captains over them all. And the Egyptians pursued the Israelites, all of Pharaoh's horses and chariots and his horsemen and his army, and they soon overtook the great host of men, women, and children at their encampment near the Red Sea.

When Pharaoh and his army drew near, the children of Israel lifted up their eyes and saw the Egyptians coming after them, and they were filled with fear and dismay. And the children of Israel cried out to God, and said to Moses, "Is it because there were no graves in Egypt that you have brought us out to die in the wilderness? Why have you dealt with us thus in leading us out of Egypt? Did we not say to you in Egypt, 'Let us alone so that

we may serve the Egyptians'? For it would have been better for us to keep on serving the Egyptians than to die in the wilderness."

But Moses calmed and consoled the people by saying to them, "Do not be afraid; stand firm and wait for the salvation of the Lord, which he will show you today; for the Egyptians whom you have seen today, you shall never see again. The Lord will fight for you, and you shall hold your peace." Then the Lord told Moses what to do, saying, "Why do you cry to me? Command the children of Israel to go forward. Lift up your rod, and stretch out your hand over the sea and divide it; and the children of Israel will go on dry ground through the middle of the sea. And I will harden the hearts of the Egyptians, and they will follow them into the sea; and I will triumph over Pharaoh and his whole army, his chariots, and his horsemen. And the Egyptians shall know that I am the Lord, when I have triumphed over Pharaoh, his chariots, and his horsemen."

That night God protected His people from a surprise attack from the Egyptians in the following way. The pillar of cloud which had gone before them moved and stood behind them, coming between the camp of the Egyptians and the camp of Israel. The cloud and the darkness were so dense that it was impossible for the Egyptians to pursue farther.

Then Moses stretched out his hand over the sea; and the Lord pushed the sea back by a strong east wind all that night, and made a

81

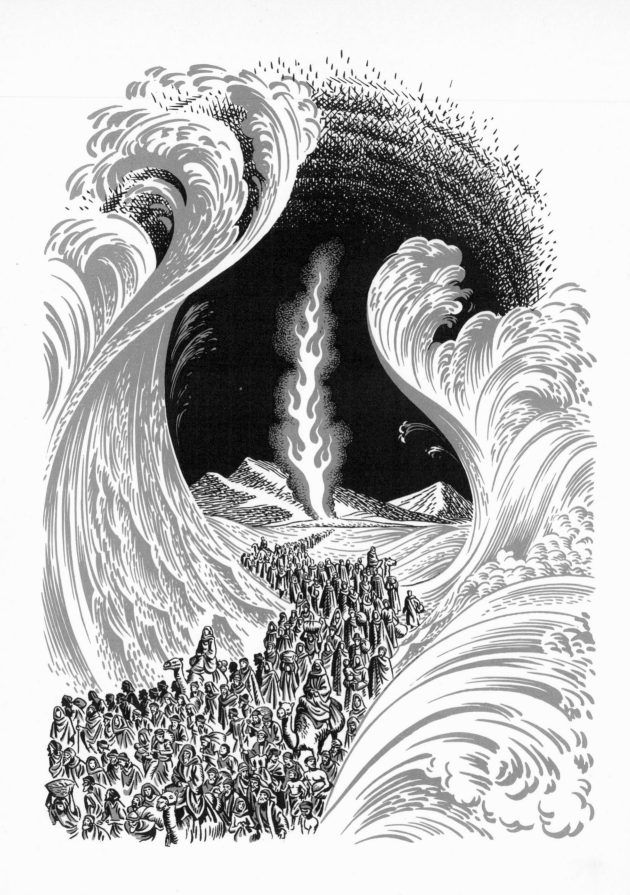

The children of Israel went into the midst of the sea on the dry ground

dry path through the sea where the waters were divided. The children of Israel went into the midst of the sea on the dry ground, and the waters formed a wall on their right hand and on their left.

The pursuing Egyptians went in after them into the midst of the sea, all Pharaoh's horses, his chariots, and his horsemen. And in the early morning the Lord looked down upon the host of the Egyptians through the pillar of fire and of cloud, and impeded their progress. Their chariot wheels were clogged and bound so that they drove heavily. The Egyptians realized that something was wrong and said, "Let us flee from the face of Israel; for the Lord is fighting for them against the Egyptians."

Then the Lord said to Moses, "Stretch out your hand over the sea, so that the waters will come again upon the Egyptians, upon their chariots, and upon their horsemen." Moses obeyed the word of the Lord, and the sea returned to its normal strength when the morning appeared; and the Egyptians fled into the rising water, and the Lord overthrew the Egyptians in the middle of the sea. And the wall of waters returned and covered the chariots and the horsemen and the whole army of Pharaoh that had followed them into the sea; and all were engulfed by the flood of waters and drowned in the middle of the sea. But the children of Israel walked on dry ground in the midst of the sea, and the waters formed a wall on their right hand and on their left.

Thus the Lord God saved Israel that day from the hand of the Egyptians. And the Israelites saw the dead bodies of the Egyptians washed up on the seashore. And they saw the great work which the Lord did against the Egyptians, and had a new fear and reverence for the God of Israel; and they believed in the Lord and in his servant Moses.

Then Moses and the children of Israel sang a song of praise and triumph to the Lord for having delivered them from the hands of the Egyptians. They were so thankful and joyful for their deliverance that they had to express their feelings in singing and dancing. Lifting up their voices in exultant praise, they sang:

"I will sing to the Lord, for He has triumphed
        gloriously;
    the horse and His rider has He thrown into
        the sea.
The Lord is my strength and song,
    and He has become my salvation;
    He is my God, and I will prepare Him a
        habitation;
    my father's God, and I will exalt Him."

TWENTY-FIVE

Moses Receives the Ten Commandments

Exodus 19:1–20:17

THREE months after the people of Israel had gone forth out of the land of Egypt, they came into the wilderness of Sinai. They made their camp at the base of Mount Horeb, which is also called Mount Sinai. This was the region where Moses had tended the flocks of Jethro, more than forty years before. And it was at Mount Horeb that God had called to Moses out of the burning bush. So now Moses led the children of Israel where before he had led the flocks of his father-in-law Jethro.

And Moses went up the mountain to commune with God, and the Lord spoke to him out of the mountain, saying, "Thus shall you speak to the house of Jacob, and tell the children of Israel: 'You have seen what I did to the Egyptians, and how I bore you on eagles' wings and brought you to myself. Now therefore, if you will obey my voice indeed, and keep my covenant, then you shall be a peculiar treasure to me above all people; for all the earth is mine, and you shall be to me a kingdom of priests and a holy nation.' These are the words which you shall speak to the children of Israel."

So Moses came down from the mountain and called the elders of the people, and laid before them all these words which the Lord had commanded him. And all the people answered together and said, "All that the Lord has spoken we will do." Again the Lord spoke to Moses, saying, "Lo, I come to you in a thick cloud, so that the people may hear when I speak with you, and believe you forever."

Then God commanded Moses to sanctify the people and have them prepare themselves for the day of revelation that was coming. The Lord said to Moses, "Go to the people and sanctify them today and tomorrow, and let them wash their clothes, and be ready for the third day; for the third day the Lord will come down upon Mount Sinai in the sight of all the people. And you shall set bounds for the people round about, saying, 'Take heed that you do not go up into the mountain, or touch the border of it; for whoever touches the mountain shall be surely put to death. If any hand should touch it, he shall surely be stoned, or shot through; whether it be beast or man, he shall not live.' When the trumpet sounds loud and long, they shall come up to the mountain."

So the people sanctified themselves, and on the morning of the third day assembled at the foot of the mountain. And there were thunders and lightnings, and a thick cloud upon the mountain. And Mount Sinai was enveloped by smoke, because the Lord descended upon it in fire; and the whole mountain quaked greatly.

And when the trumpet sounded long and grew louder and louder, Moses spoke, and God answered him with a crash of thunder. And the Lord came down upon Mount Sinai, to the top of the mountain; and the Lord called Moses to the top of the mountain, and Moses went up. And the Lord said to Moses,

God gave Moses the Ten Commandments

"Go down and caution the people, lest they break through to the Lord to gaze and many of them perish. And also let the priests who come near to the Lord sanctify themselves, lest the Lord break forth upon them."

And Moses said to the Lord, "The people cannot come up to Mount Sinai; for you commanded us yourself, saying, 'Set bounds about the mountain, and sanctify it.'" And the Lord said to Moses, "Go down, and bring Aaron up with you; but do not let the priests and the people break through to come up to the Lord, lest He break forth upon them." So Moses went down to the people and told them what the Lord had said.

After this Moses went up into the mountain and communed with God for forty days. And God gave to Moses the Ten Commandments, written on tablets of stone, which Moses in turn gave to the people. These are the words God spoke to Moses as a message for all time:

I am the Lord thy God, who brought thee out of the land of Egypt, out of the house of bondage. Thou shalt have no other gods before me.

Thou shalt not make unto thee any graven image, or any likeness of anything that is in heaven above, or that is in the earth beneath, or that is in the water under the earth. Thou shalt not bow down thyself to them, nor serve them; for I the Lord thy God am a jealous God, visiting the iniquity of the fathers upon the children unto the third and fourth generation of them that hate me; and showing mercy unto thousands of them that love me, and keep my commandments.

Thou shalt not take the name of the Lord thy God in vain; for the Lord will not hold him guiltless that taketh His name in vain.

Remember the sabbath day, to keep it holy. Six days shalt thou labor, and do all thy work; but the seventh day is the sabbath of the Lord thy God: in it thou shalt not do any work, thou, nor thy son, nor thy daughter, thy manservant, nor thy maidservant, nor thy cattle, nor thy stranger that is within thy gates. For in six days the Lord made heaven and earth, the sea, and all that in them is, and rested the seventh day: wherefore the Lord blessed the sabbath day, and hallowed it.

Honor thy father and thy mother: that thy days may be long upon the land which the Lord thy God giveth thee.

Thou shalt not kill.

Thou shalt not commit adultery.

Thou shalt not steal.

Thou shalt not bear false witness against thy neighbor.

Thou shalt not covet thy neighbor's house, thou shalt not covet thy neighbor's wife, nor his manservant, nor his maidservant, nor his ox, nor his ass, nor anything that is thy neighbor's.

TWENTY-SIX

Aaron Makes the Golden Calf

Exodus 32:1–35

WHEN the people of Israel saw that Moses stayed up in the mountain for so long a time, they became very impatient and restless. Instead of having faith in their great leader, they began to doubt and distrust him. They gathered together before Aaron the priest and said to him, "Come now, make us gods, who shall go before us; as for this Moses, the man who brought us up out of the land of Egypt, we do not know what has happened to him."

Aaron should have rebuked the people and refused their request, but he did not. Instead he said to the people, "Remove the golden earrings which your wives, your sons, and your daughters are wearing, and bring them to me." The people did as Aaron told them. And Aaron received the gold trinkets from them, and fashioned them together into a molten calf, and presented this idol of gold to the people. And they cried, "These are your gods, O Israel, who brought you up out of the land of Egypt." When Aaron saw how the people worshiped the golden calf, he built an altar before it, and proclaimed a feast to the Lord the following day. And the people rose up early on the next day, and offered burnt offerings and brought peace offerings; and they sat down to eat and drink, and rose up to play.

While this was going on, the Lord spoke to Moses in the mountain, saying, "Go down right away, for your people, whom you brought out of the land of Egypt, have corrupted themselves; they have turned aside quickly out of the way which I commanded them: they have made for themselves a molten calf, and have worshiped it and sacrificed to it, and said, 'These are your gods, O Israel, who brought you up out of the land of Egypt.' " The Lord also said to Moses, "I have seen this people, and behold, it is a stiff-necked people; now therefore let me alone, so that my wrath may grow hot against them and I may consume them; and I will make of you a great nation."

But Moses prayed to the Lord on behalf of the people, and asked God to withhold judgment upon them. He prayed to God to remember His covenant with Abraham, Isaac, and Jacob to multiply their progeny, and to give them an inheritance in the Promised Land. The Lord heard the prayer of Moses, and withheld the evil which He thought to do to His people.

Then Moses went down the mountain carrying the two tablets of the law in his hands, tablets that were written on both sides. And the tablets were the work of God, and the writing was the writing of God, graven upon the tablets. When Joshua, who was with Moses, heard the shouting of the people, he said, "There is a noise of war in the camp." But Moses said, "It is not the noise of victory, nor the noise of defeat, but the noise of singing that I hear." And as soon as he came near the camp and saw the golden calf and

The people worshiped the golden calf

the idolatrous dancing, Moses' anger grew hot, and he flung the tablets of the law out of his hands and broke them at the foot of the mountain. And Moses took the molten calf, and burned it with fire, and ground it to powder, and strewed it upon the water, and made the people of Israel drink it.

Then Moses rebuked Aaron, saying, "What did this people do to you that you have brought so great a sin upon them?" Aaron tried to excuse himself by saying, "Let not the anger of my lord grow hot; you know the people, and how they are bent on doing evil. For they said to me, 'Make us gods, who shall go before us; as for this Moses, we do not know what has happened to him.' And I said to them, 'Let those who wear gold remove it.' So they gave it to me, and I threw it into the fire, and there came out this calf."

When Moses saw that both Aaron and the people were to blame for this wickedness, he decided to test their loyalty to the God of Israel. So Moses stood in the gate of the camp and said, "Who is on the Lord's side? Let him come to me." And all the sons of Levi gathered themselves together to him. Then Moses directed the sons of Levi to punish the disobedient idolaters. The result was that three thousand people were slain.

The next day Moses assembled the people and said to them, "You have committed a great sin. And now I will go up to the Lord; perhaps I will be able to make atonement for your sin." So Moses spoke to God in the mountain and said, "Alas, this people have committed a great sin; they have fashioned gods of gold for themselves. Yet now, if only you will forgive their sin—and if not, blot me, I pray you, out of your book which you have written." But the Lord said to Moses, "Whoever has sinned against me, him will I blot out of my book. Therefore go now, lead the people to the place of which I have spoken to you; behold, my angel will go before you. Nevertheless, in the day when I visit, I will visit their sin upon them."

And the Lord sent down a plague upon the people for worshiping the golden calf.

TWENTY-SEVEN

Moses Sends the Twelve Spies to Canaan

Numbers 13:1–14:45

THE children of Israel left the region of Mount Sinai, and continued their journey for several days through the wilderness of Paran until they came to the southern border of Canaan, to a place called Kadesh. There, according to the word of the Lord, Moses chose twelve men, representing the twelve tribes of Israel, and sent them forth to spy out the land of Canaan. The names of the twelve spies are all given, but Caleb and Joshua are the two best known to us.

Moses instructed the twelve men to go into the Negeb, or southern country, and to make a careful inspection of the land, the people, the cities, the camps, the forests, the crops, and other natural resources. He also asked them to bring some of the fruit of the land with them when they returned.

So the twelve men went forth, and secretly traveled through the land of Canaan from the south to the north and then back again, taking forty days for the journey. On the return journey they came to the brook of Eshcol, where they cut a branch with one cluster of grapes so large that it had to be carried on a pole between two men. They also gathered some fine figs and pomegranates which they brought back with them.

At the end of forty days they returned from spying out the land. And they came to Moses and Aaron and to all the children of Israel who were assembled at Kadesh, in the wilderness of Paran. The spies brought back word of what they had seen and done, and showed the people the fruit of the land which they had brought. Then some of the spies gave this report to Moses: "We went through the land to which you sent us; truly it flows with milk and honey, and this is its fruit. But the people who dwell in the land are very strong, and the cities are walled and very great; and moreover, we saw the children of Anak there."

Then Caleb, a man of great faith and courage, quieted the people before Moses, and said, "Let us go up at once and possess it; for we are well able to overcome it."

But ten of the men who had gone up with Caleb and Joshua spoke against Caleb's plan, saying, "We are not able to go up against the people; for they are much stronger than we are. The land which we traveled through and searched out is a land that devours its inhabitants; and all the people that we saw in it are men of great stature. And there we saw the giant sons of Anak; and we felt like grass-hoppers in their sight." Thus they brought to Moses and the people an unfavorable report of the land of Canaan.

The people were very sad and discouraged when they heard this unfavorable report, and they wept all night. They began to murmur and complain against Moses and Aaron, and they cried, "Would God that we had died in the land of Egypt! Or would God that we had died in this wilderness! Why has the Lord brought us into this land only to fall by the sword, and so that our wives and our children should become a prey? Would it not be better for us to return to Egypt?"

And the people said to one another, "Let us choose a captain, and let us return to Egypt." Moses and Aaron were grieved with the people for their disobedience and unbelief. And Joshua and Caleb pleaded with the people not to rebel against the Lord, but to trust Him to bring them safely into the land of Canaan. But the people would not listen to Caleb and Joshua, and wanted to stone them to death.

But at this point the glory of the Lord appeared at the tabernacle of the congregation before all the children of Israel. And the Lord spoke to Moses, saying that He would punish the people for their disobedience and unbelief. But Moses prayed to God on behalf of the people, saying, "O Lord, pardon, I beseech you, the iniquity of this people, according to the greatness of your mercy, and as you have forgiven this people from Egypt even until now."

The Lord heard the prayer of Moses, and pardoned the people according to his word. But the Lord also decreed that none of those who had disbelieved God's promise should live to see the land of Canaan, because they had openly despised the Lord. Then God said to Moses, "But my servant Caleb, because he was of another spirit and followed me faithfully, him will I bring into the land into which he went, and his children shall inherit it. Now, seeing that the Amalekites and Canaanites live in the valley, turn tomorrow and go into the wilderness by way of the Red Sea."

So the children of Israel were turned back from Kadesh to wander in the wilderness for forty years as punishment for their sinful disobedience and open rebellion against the Lord. For each of the forty days required to spy out the land, for each day a year, the people were to suffer the results of their iniquity and the Lord's displeasure. All of their number above twenty years of age who had murmured against the Lord were condemned to die in the wilderness before reaching the Promised Land.

The ten men who had brought an unfavorable report of the land were smitten with the plague and died. But Joshua the son of Nun and Caleb the son of Jephunneh remained alive, because they had brought a good report.

Then the people decided they would go up into the hills and fight against the Canaanites and possess the land. But Moses warned them not to do this, because the Lord was not with them. But they did not heed Moses, and went up into the hills; however, neither the ark of the covenant of the Lord, nor Moses, departed from the camp. Then the Amalekites and the Canaanites came down, and defeated the Israelites, and harried them for a long way into the wilderness, even to Hormah.

The spies showed the fruit of the land which they had brought

TWENTY-EIGHT

Moses Lifts Up the Brazen Serpent

Numbers 20:23; 21:1–9

THE whole congregation of the people of Israel journeyed on from Kadesh until they came to Mount Hor. And the Lord said to Moses and Aaron at Mount Hor, on the border of the land of Edom, "Now Aaron shall be gathered to his people; he shall not enter into the land which I have given to the children of Israel because you rebelled against my word at the waters of Meribah. Take Aaron, and Eleazar his son, and bring them up to Mount Hor; and strip Aaron of his garments, and put them upon Eleazar his son; and Aaron shall be gathered to his people and shall die there."

And Moses did as the Lord commanded him, and they went up Mount Hor in the sight of all the congregation. And Moses stripped Aaron of his priestly garments and put them upon Eleazar his son; and Aaron died there on the top of the mountain. Then Moses and Eleazar came down from the mountain. And when all the congregation saw that Aaron was dead, all the house of Israel mourned for Aaron thirty days.

When the Canaanite king of Arad, a town on the southern border of Judah, heard that the Israelites were coming through his territory, he fought against them and took some of them prisoner. But the Israelites turned to God with renewed faith, and said, "If you will indeed deliver these Canaanites into our hands, then we will utterly destroy their cities." And the Lord heeded their prayer, and gave them the victory over the Canaan-

ites. And the warriors of Israel conquered the Canaanites, and destroyed their cities; so the name of the place was called Hormah, which means "utter destruction."

From Mount Hor the children of Israel journeyed on by way of the Red Sea, to go around the land of Edom. And again the people became restless and impatient on the way. In a distrustful and complaining mood they spoke against God and against Moses, saying, "Why have you brought us up out of Egypt only to die in the wilderness? For there is no bread and no water, and we loathe this light bread." Then, to punish the people for their sinful disobedience, the Lord sent fiery serpents among them; and they bit the people, and many of them died. In a fearful and penitent mood the people came to Moses and pleaded with him, saying, "We have sinned, for we have spoken against the Lord and against you; pray to the Lord to take away the serpents from us."

So Moses prayed to God on behalf of the people. And the Lord said to Moses, "Make an image of a fiery serpent and set it on a pole; and everyone who is bitten, when he looks upon it, shall live." So Moses made a serpent of brass and lifted it up on a pole; and when a serpent bit any man, if he looked at the serpent of brass, he lived.

When Moses was a hundred and twenty years old, God commanded him to go up to Mount Nebo in the land of Moab across the River Jordan from the land of Canaan. The

The serpent of brass was lifted up on a pole

Lord then said to Moses, "Behold the land of Canaan, which I give to the children of Israel for a possession. You must die on the mount and be gathered to your people, as Aaron your brother died on Mount Hor and was gathered to his people."

And Moses went up from the plains of Moab to Mount Nebo, and the Lord said to him, "This is the land which I promised to Abraham, to Isaac, and to Jacob, saying, I will give it to your descendants. I have caused you to see it with your eyes, but you shall not go over there."

So Moses died in the land of Moab. And the children of Israel wept and mourned for Moses for thirty days.

III.

STORIES

ABOUT JOSHUA

AND THE

JUDGES

Rahab bound the scarlet cord in the window

TWENTY-NINE

Joshua Sends the Spies to Jericho

Joshua 1:1–2:24

AFTER the death of Moses, God spoke to Joshua the son of Nun and directed him to lead the Israelites across the Jordan River and into the land of Canaan. God promised Joshua that He would be with him even as He had been with Moses, and that He would give Joshua the victory over all their enemies. Joshua was commanded to obey the laws of God, even as Moses had done, in order to have success in the conquest of Canaan. The Lord assured Joshua of His blessing, saying, "Have not I commanded you? Be strong and of good courage; be not afraid, neither be dismayed; for the Lord your God is with you wherever you go."

Then Joshua commanded the officers of the people, saying, "Pass through the camp and command the people, 'Prepare your food; for within three days you shall pass over this Jordan, to go in to take possession of the land which the Lord your God gives you to possess.'" While the people were preparing to start, Joshua sent two men secretly across the Jordan to spy out the land and to learn all they could about the fortified city of Jericho. Joshua realized that it would be necessary to conquer this strong city before they could proceed further into the land of Canaan.

Joshua's two spies came to Jericho and entered into the gate of the city, where they found lodging in the house of a woman by the name of Rahab. But someone saw them and reported to the king of Jericho that certain men of Israel had come to spy out the land. The king of Jericho hastily sent messengers to Rahab, saying, "Bring forth the men who have come to you and entered your house; for they have come to search out all our country."

But Rahab believed that Joshua's men were servants of the God of Israel, and she felt duty-bound to protect them from the evil intentions of the king of Jericho. So she took the two men up to the flat roof of her house, and hid them with stalks of flax which she laid in order upon the roof. Then she misdirected the king's officers by pretending that the spies had gone forth out of the city at nightfall. So the officers went out of the city and pursued the men as far as the fords of the Jordan.

Then Rahab went up on the roof and talked with the men of Israel and explained why she had befriended them. She said she knew the Lord was about to give the Israelites possession of their land. She had heard what wonderful things the Lord had done for the Israelites in bringing them out of Egypt and in leading them safely through the Red Sea. She believed the God of the Israelites to be the God of heaven and of earth, and she wished to serve their God.

Then she asked Joshua's men to make a

covenant with her, saying, "Now therefore, I pray you, swear to me by the Lord that since I have showed kindness to you, you will also show kindness to my father's house, and give me a true sign that you will save alive my father and mother, my brothers and sisters, and all that they have, and save us from death." The men agreed to her request, saying, "Our life for yours. If you do not betray our plans, then we will deal kindly and truly with you when the Lord gives us the land."

Whereupon Rahab let the two men down by a rope through the window to the outside of the wall, for her house was built as a part of the city wall. She bade them go into the hills and hide themselves from their pursuers for three days, and then return to their camp. Before leaving, the men asked Rahab to mark her house by binding a scarlet cord in the win-

dow so that they would know which house was to be spared when the soldiers of Joshua invaded the city. Then she sent the men away, and they departed; and she bound the scarlet cord in the window as she had promised she would do.

The two men went into the hills, as Rahab had directed them, and stayed there three days. When their pursuers had given up the search for them, they came down from the hills, passed over the Jordan, and came to Joshua their commander. They reported fully to Joshua all that had befallen them and how Rahab had befriended and protected them. They concluded their report by saying to Joshua, "Truly the Lord has delivered all the land into our hands; for even the inhabitants of the country are fearful and fainthearted because of us."

THIRTY

Joshua Leads Israel Across the Jordan

Joshua 3:1–4:24

As JOSHUA had commanded, the children of Israel prepared for the great day when they should cross over the Jordan River and enter into the Promised Land. They prepared food to last for several days, and were all packed and ready to march at Joshua's command. At Joshua's word they broke camp in the plains of Moab, where they had camped for several months, and moved to the banks of the Jor-

dan. There they lodged in their tents for three days until they were ready to pass over the river. On the eve of this great historic event, Joshua said to the people, "Sanctify yourselves, for tomorrow the Lord will do wonders among you."

Early in the morning the great procession formed according to the plan Joshua had received from the Lord. The priests went first, bearing the ark of the covenant, and were followed by the people and the armed warriors.

The waters of the Jordan were full to overflowing, and without a miracle of God's power it would have been impossible for the people to cross the rushing river. But God had told Joshua what to do and what to expect. So according to the word of the Lord, when the priests bearing the ark touched their feet in the brink of the water, the waters stopped coming down from above and formed a high wall farther up the river. The water flowing down quickly ran away, leaving a dry river bed through which the people could walk.

And the priests who bore the ark of the covenant stood firm on dry ground in the middle of the Jordan until all the people of Israel had crossed over.

When all the people had crossed safely over the Jordan, the Lord spoke to Joshua, saying, "Take twelve men from among the people, one man from each tribe, and command them to take twelve stones from the midst of the Jordan, from the very place where the priests' feet stood firm; and bear them over with you

The priests who bore the ark of the covenant stood on dry ground in the middle of the Jordan

and put them down in the place where you shall lodge tonight." The men of Israel did as Joshua commanded, according to the word of the Lord. Joshua also set up twelve stones in the midst of the Jordan, in the place where the priests bearing the ark of God had stood.

The people crossed over Jordan as rapidly as they could; and when they had passed over, the priests bearing the ark of the Lord left their station in the river bed and passed over before the people. And about forty thousand men equipped for war passed over before the Lord to battle, to the plains of Jericho. On that day the Lord glorified Joshua in the sight of all Israel; and they feared him, as they had feared Moses, all the days of his life.

When the priests bearing the ark of the covenant of the Lord came up from the midst of the Jordan, and the soles of the priests' feet were lifted up on dry land, the waters of the Jordan returned to their place and overflowed all its banks, as before.

The people crossed over into the land of Canaan on the tenth day of the first month and encamped in Gilgal, on the east border of Jericho. And the twelve stones which they had taken out of the Jordan, Joshua put down in Gilgal. And he said to the children of Israel, "When your children ask their fathers in time to come, 'What do these stones mean?' then you shall tell your children how Israel crossed over this Jordan on dry ground. For the Lord your God dried up the waters of the Jordan from before you, until you had crossed over, as the Lord your God did to the Red Sea, which he dried up from before us until we had gone over, so that all the people of the earth might know that the hand of the Lord is mighty, and that you might fear the Lord your God forever."

THIRTY-ONE

Joshua Captures the Walled City of Jericho

Joshua 5:13–6:27

ONE day Joshua went forth from the camp at Gilgal to view the walled city of Jericho and to plan how he could best attack this strongly fortified city. Suddenly Joshua looked up, and behold, a man stood before him with a drawn sword in his hand. Joshua wondered at this, and said to the Stranger, "Are you for the Israelites, or for the people of Jericho?" The Stranger replied, "Not so; but I have now come as commander of the army of the Lord."

When Joshua realized that God had sent this messenger to him, he fell on his face to the earth in an attitude of worship and obeisance. Then Joshua asked, "What does my lord bid his servant to do?" And the commander of the army of the Lord said to Joshua, "Take off your shoes; for the place

The stone wall around Jericho trembled and fell down with a great crashing sound

where you stand is holy ground." Joshua quickly obeyed, just as Moses had done before him at the burning bush. As a result of this experience, Joshua knew that the Lord would give him the victory over the city of Jericho.

The commander of the army of the Lord told Joshua the plan of attack against the great walled city. On the day appointed, all the men of war were to march around the walls of the city once. A large company of soldiers was to lead the march. Then seven priests blowing trumpets of rams' horns were to follow. Four other priests bearing the ark of the Lord were to come next. Other thousands of armed warriors and the people were to complete the great procession. This plan of march was to be repeated once a day for six days in succession. On the seventh day they were to circle the city seven times, the priests blowing the trumpets. When they had done this, the priests were to blow a long blast with the ram's horn, and all the people were to shout with a mighty shout. Then the walls of the city would fall down, and the soldiers were to rush in and capture the city.

Joshua's commands were carried out to the letter. The seven priests bearing the seven trumpets of rams' horns went forward before the Lord, and blew the trumpets; and the ark of the covenant of the Lord followed them. And the armed men went before the priests who blew the trumpets, and the rear guard came after the ark, while the trumpets continued to blow. But Joshua had commanded the people, saying, "You shall not shout or make any sound with your voices, neither shall any word proceed out of your mouths, until the day I bid you shout; then you shall shout."

So the ark of the Lord encircled the city,

going about it once; and they returned to the camp and spent the night there.

The second day they circled the city once, and returned to the camp. So they did for six days.

On the seventh day they rose at dawn, and circled the city in the same manner seven times: only on that day did they circle the city seven times. And the seventh time, when the priests had blown the trumpets, Joshua commanded the people, "Shout; for the Lord has given you the city." When the people heard the sound of the trumpet, with one accord they raised a great and mighty shout. And the great stone wall around Jericho trembled and shook and fell down flat with a great rumbling and crashing sound!

Then the warriors of the Israelites turned and rushed into the city and put to death by the edge of the sword all of the inhabitants of the city, both men and women, young and old. They also slaughtered the oxen, sheep, and asses, as Joshua had commanded.

For Joshua had warned the people in advance, saying, "The city and all that is within it shall be given up to the Lord for destruction. Only Rahab and her family shall live, because she hid the messengers that we sent. But you are not to keep for yourselves any of the things dedicated to destruction, lest you bring trouble upon the camp of Israel. But all the silver and gold, and vessels of brass and iron, are consecrated to the Lord; they shall go into the treasury of the Lord."

Then Joshua said to the two men who had spied out the land, "Go into Rahab's house, and bring her and the members of her family out safely, even as you swore to her." So the young men who had been spies went in, and brought out Rahab, and her father and mother and brothers, and all that she had, and took them to a place of safety outside the camp of Israel.

Then the soldiers of Joshua burned the fallen city, and all that was in it, with fire. Only the silver and gold, and the vessels of brass and iron, were put into the treasury of the house of the Lord. But Joshua saved Rahab alive, and her father's household and all that she had. And she dwelt in Israel the rest of her life, and served the God of Israel in other ways. She was permitted to do this because she hid the messengers whom Joshua had sent to spy out Jericho.

The Lord continued to bless Joshua; and his fame was reported throughout all the land. When Joshua died, at the age of a hundred and ten, he was buried in Timnath-serah, in Mount Ephraim.

THIRTY-TWO

Gideon Is Called to Deliver Israel

Judges 6:1–24

DURING the period of the Judges, the children of Israel again and again did that which was evil in the sight of the Lord. They forsook the Lord God of their fathers and followed other gods, the gods of the people that were round about them, and bowed to them, and served Baal. First Mesopotamia, then Moab, then Canaan warred against and conquered Israel. Each time the people repented, and the Lord delivered them from their oppressors. Next came Midian.

For a period of seven years the Midianites prevailed over Israel and chastised the people. They came from the land east of Israel and swarmed over the country. They ravaged the crops Israel had planted; drove off all their sheep, oxen, and asses; consumed or destroyed all the produce of the land, and even drove the Israelites from their homes and fields. During this time the oppressed Israelites sought refuge and safety in the dens and caves of mountain strongholds. The people of Israel were reduced to poverty by the ravages of the Midianites, and they cried out to the Lord for help.

When the children of Israel thus showed signs of repentance, the Lord sent them a prophet who spoke to them the message that they needed to hear. He reminded them of God's goodness and mercy to them in the past. He showed them that these new troubles had come upon them because they had forsaken the God of Israel. He declared that the false gods they had been worshiping could not help them.

One day after the prophet had spoken these things, a young man of the Israelites by the name of Gideon, the son of Joash, was threshing wheat in the wine press, to hide it from the

The angel of the Lord told Gideon to save Israel from the Midianites

Midianites. An angel of the Lord sat under an oak and appeared to Gideon and said, "The Lord is with you, you mighty man of valor."

Gideon did not yet know that the speaker was the angel of the Lord, and he replied, "Oh, my Lord, if the Lord is with us, why then has all this befallen us? And where are all his miraculous works of which our fathers told us, saying, 'Did not the Lord bring us up from Egypt?' But now the Lord has forsaken us, and delivered us into the hands of the Midianites."

And the angel of the Lord turned to him and said, "Go in this might of yours and save Israel from the hands of the Midianites; have I not sent you?" But Gideon tried to excuse himself, saying, "Oh, my Lord, how can I save Israel? Behold, my family is the poorest in Manasseh, and I am the least in my father's house."

Then the Lord said to Gideon, "Surely I will be with you and you shall destroy the Midianites as one man." Gideon answered, "If now I have found favor in your sight, then show me a sign that it is you who are talking with me. Do not depart from here, I pray you, until I come to you, and bring forth my present, and set it before you." And the messenger of the Lord said, "I will await your return."

So Gideon went off, and got ready a kid, and unleavened cakes from a measure of flour. He put the meat in a basket, and he put the broth in a pot, and brought them to the messenger under the oak tree and presented them. And the angel of God said to Gideon, "Take the meat and the unleavened cakes, and lay them upon this rock, and pour the broth over them." Gideon did as he was directed. Then the angel of the Lord touched the meat and the unleavened cakes with the end of the staff that was in his hand, and there shot forth fire from the rock and consumed the meat and the unleavened cakes. Then the angel of the Lord vanished from his sight.

When Gideon perceived that his visitor was the angel of the Lord, he cried out, saying, "Alas, O Lord my God! For now I have seen an angel of the Lord face to face." But the Lord reassured Gideon, saying, "Peace be with you; fear not: you shall not die." Then Gideon built at that sacred spot an altar to the Lord, and called it Jehovah-shalom, which means "the Lord send peace." For a long time afterward the altar which Gideon built stood by the oak of Ophrah, in the region which belonged to Joash the Abiezrite.

THIRTY-THREE

Gideon Destroys the Altar of Baal

Judges 6:25–40

THAT same night, after the angel had appeared to Gideon at the oak of Ophrah, the Lord spoke again to Gideon and commanded him to pull down the altar of Baal which Joash his father had erected on his own property. Apparently Gideon's father was a leader of the people in this idolatrous worship.

Since God had called Gideon to deliver Israel from the oppression of the Midianites, the people had to be recalled to worship and serve the true God of Israel. Hence the Lord said to Gideon, "Take your father's young bullock, the second bullock seven years old, and throw down the altar of Baal which your father has, and cut down the grove of trees that is next to it. In its place you are to build an altar to the Lord your God upon the top of this rock, with stones laid in their proper order; then take the second bullock, and offer it as a burnt sacrifice with the wood of the trees which you shall cut down."

So Gideon at once took ten of his menservants, and did as the Lord commanded him. But because he feared his father's household and the men of the city too much to do it openly in the daytime, Gideon did it secretly by night.

When the men of the city arose early the next morning, they saw that the altar of Baal had been thrown down, and that the grove of trees beside it had been cut down. They also saw the new altar which had been built, and the offering which had been laid upon it. And they said to one another, "Who has done this?" And when they had inquired and made search, they declared, "Gideon the son of Joash has done this thing."

Then the men of the city demanded of Joash, "Bring out your son, so that he may die, because he has thrown down the altar of Baal and cut down the grove of trees that was next to it." But Joash, realizing that God was working through his son, boldly replied, "Will you take sides with Baal? Will you plead his cause? Whoever takes sides with him, let him be put to death while it is still morning. If Baal is a god, let him plead for himself, because his altar has been thrown down." Therefore on that day Gideon was called Jerubbaal, which means "let Baal plead against him," because Gideon had thrown down the altar of Baal.

At this time the Midianites and the Amalekites and the children of the East came together, and crossed the Jordan and pitched camp in the Valley of Jezreel. Whereupon the Spirit of the Lord came upon Gideon; and he blew a trumpet, and the Abiezrites came together to follow him. And Gideon sent messengers throughout all Manasseh; and they too came together to follow him. He also sent messengers to Asher, to Zebulun, and to Naphtali; and they went up to meet them.

Gideon asked God to show him a sign. And Gideon said to the Lord, "If you will save Israel by my hand, as you have said, behold, I will put a fleece of wool on the thresh-

Gideon did as the Lord commanded him

ing floor; if there is dew on the fleece only, and it is dry on all the ground beside it, then I shall know that you will save Israel by my hand, as you have said."

God heard Gideon's prayer and answered it. When Gideon rose early the next morning and twisted the fleece, he squeezed enough dew from it to fill a bowl of water. Then Gideon said to God, "Let not your anger be hot

against me, and I will speak but this once; let me make a test, I pray you, just once more with the fleece; this time let it be dry only on the fleece, on the ground let there be dew." And God did as Gideon requested that night; for it was dry on the fleece only, and there was dew on all the ground. So Gideon knew that the Lord was with him, and God would give His people the victory over their oppressors.

THIRTY-FOUR

Gideon Chooses His Army of Three Hundred

Judges 7:1-15

GIDEON's blowing of the trumpet and sending of messengers to the various tribes of Israel brought thirty-two thousand men together in response to their leader's stirring call. This great throng came together and encamped at a place beside the well of Harod, not far from Jezreel. The camp of the Midianites was to the north of them, by the hill of Moreh, in the valley.

Then the Lord said to Gideon, "The people who are with you are too many for me to give the Midianites into their hands, lest Israel belittle me, saying, 'My own hand has saved me.' Now therefore go, and proclaim in the ears of the people, saying, 'Whoever is fearful and afraid, let him depart from Mount Gilead and return home.'" When Gideon thus tested them, twenty-two thousand returned to their

homes; only ten thousand of them remained.

But again the Lord spoke to Gideon, saying, "There are still too many people; bring them down to the water, and I will test them for you there. And he of whom I say to you, 'This man shall go with you,' the same shall go with you; and of whomever I say to you, 'This man shall not go with you,' the same shall not go."

So Gideon brought the throng of ten thousand down to the water. Then the Lord showed Gideon the plan by which he was to test and further reduce his army. Every man that lapped the water with one hand, while holding his weapon in the other hand, was to be set apart on one side. And every man who laid aside his weapon, and knelt down to drink of the water, was to be set apart on the other side. And behold, the number of those that

The test revealed the three hundred men who were most alert and vigilant

lapped, putting their hands to their mouths, was three hundred men. But all the rest of the ten thousand knelt down to drink water out of the stream. This strange test revealed the three hundred men who were most alert and vigilant, and who took not the slightest chance of being caught off guard by the enemy. The test may also have indicated that the three hundred men who did not kneel down to drink were those who were not in the habit of bowing their knees in the worship of Baal. Thus they were God's faithful servants, ready to fight the Lord's battles.

At any rate, the Lord said to Gideon, "With the help of the three hundred men that lapped I will save you, and deliver the Midianites into your hand. Let all the other people go, every man back to his tent." So the people took their provisions, and their trumpets; and Gideon sent all the rest of Israel back, every man to his tent, but retained the three hundred men as his chosen army. And the camp of the Midianites was sprawled out in the valley below him.

That same night the Lord said to Gideon, "Arise, go down to the Midianites' camp; for I have delivered it into your hand. If you are afraid to go down alone, take Phurah your servant with you. There you shall hear what they say, and afterward your hands shall be strengthened to go down to attack the camp."

Then Gideon went down with Phurah his servant to the outposts of the camp of armed men. And the Midianites and the Amalekites and all the children of the East lay along the valley like grasshoppers for multitude; and their camels were without number, like the sands by the seaside for multitude.

As Gideon and his servant stealthily approached the camp, they overheard a man telling a dream to his comrade. And the man said, "Behold, I dreamed a dream; and lo, a cake of barley bread tumbled into the camp of the Midianites, and came into a tent, and struck it so that it fell, and overturned it, so that the tent lay flat on the ground." And his comrade answered, "This is nothing else than the sword of Gideon the son of Joash, a man of Israel; for into his hand God has delivered the Midianites and all the host."

When Gideon heard the telling of this dream and its interpretation, he worshiped and thanked God; for by this experience he understood that God would surely give him the victory. And he hastily returned to the camp of the Israelites, and said to his soldiers, "Arise; for the Lord has delivered the camp of the Midianites into your hand."

THIRTY-FIVE

Gideon's Army Defeats the Midianites

Judges 7:16–8:28

THAT same night, in preparation for the attack upon the Midianites, Gideon divided the three hundred men into three companies; and into every man's hand he put a trumpet, an empty pitcher with a torch inside. Then he carefully instructed them what to do, saying, "Look at me, and do likewise; and behold, when I come to the outposts of the camp, do as I do. When I blow the trumpet, then all of you who are with me blow the trumpets also on every side of the camp, and shout, 'The sword of the Lord and of Gideon.'"

So Gideon and the three hundred men who were with him came to the outposts of the camp of the Midianites at the beginning of the middle watch—that is, at midnight—when they had just set the watch. Silently the three hundred men encircled the whole camp of the Midianites, as Gideon had directed them. Then, at a given signal from Gideon, they all blew the trumpets and smashed the pitchers that were in their hands. And the three companies blew the trumpets and broke the pitchers, holding the torches in their left hands, and the trumpets in their right hands to blow with. And they cried out with a mighty shout, "The sword of the Lord and of Gideon."

The sleeping Midianites were terrified at being so rudely awakened by the blast of the trumpets and the shouts of Gideon's soldiers. And seeing the flaming torches all around their camp, they thought they were being attacked by a great army of the Israelites. Suddenly they became panic-stricken and cried out in mortal terror. In the darkness and confusion, they tried to escape by fleeing from the camp. But as Gideon's three hundred warriors continued to blow their trumpets, the Lord set every Midianite's sword against his fellow, throughout the whole army. As a result, in the panic and confusion great numbers of the Midianites were slain by their own swords.

The midnight panic of the army of the Midianites became a complete rout, and they fled toward the Jordan Valley, as far as the border of Abel-meholah. And the men of Israel came together from the tribes of Naphtali and Asher and Manasseh, and joined the army of Gideon and pursued the fleeing Midianites. And Gideon sent messengers throughout the hills of Ephraim, saying, "Come down against the Midianites and seize the fords of the Jordan to prevent them from escaping." So all the men of Ephraim came together, and they seized the fords of the Jordan as far as Beth-barah. And they captured two princes of Midian, Oreb and Zeeb, and slew them.

And the men of Ephraim said to Gideon, "What have you done to us, not calling us when you went to fight with the Midianites?" And they spoke very indignantly to Gideon. But Gideon pacified them by saying, "What have I done now as compared with you? Is not the gleaning of the grapes of Ephraim better than the vintage of Abiezer? God has delivered into your hands the princes of Midian, Oreb and Zeeb; what have I been able to do

in comparison with what you have done?"
Then their anger was abated, when Gideon
said this to them.

Now Zebah and Zalmunna, two of the
kings of the Midianites, were in Karkor with
about fifteen thousand men, all that was left
of the army of the children of the East; for
there had fallen a hundred and twenty thousand men who drew the sword. And Gideon
went up by the caravan route east of Nobah
and attacked the army; for it was off guard.
And when Zebah and Zalmunna, the two
kings of Midian, fled, Gideon pursued them
and captured them, and put the army to rout.
A little later, the two kings of Midian were
slain.

After Gideon had won this notable victory
over the Midianites, the men of Israel came
to him and said, "Rule over us, you, and your
son, and your son's son also; for you have delivered us from the hand of Midian." But Gideon did not want them to make him king over
Israel. He wanted them to consider God as
their King. And so he said to the men of Israel, "I will not rule over you, neither shall
my son rule over you: the Lord shall rule over
you."

So Midian was subdued before the children
of Israel, and they lifted up their heads no
more. And the country had peace for forty
years in the days of Gideon. And Gideon
judged Israel, at the word of the Lord, for
forty years. And Gideon the son of Joash died
in a good old age, and was buried in the tomb
of Joash his father, at Ophrah of the Abiezrites.

THIRTY-SIX

Samson's Birth and Mission

Judges 13:1-25

ABOUT eighty years had passed since the
death of Gideon. Following Gideon, a number of other Judges
ruled over Israel, about seven in
all. However, the people of Israel again did
that which was evil in the sight of the Lord.
They relapsed into idolatry, and worshiped
the false gods of the heathen tribes around
them. Like disobedient children, they did not
seem long to remember the lessons they had
learned from God's punishments and deliv-
erances of the past.

Now it was the nation of the Philistines
that troubled and oppressed Israel for a period of forty years. The Philistines were a
strong, warlike, cruel people who lived to the
west of Israel on the coast of the Mediterranean Sea. Their chief cities were Gath,
Gaza, and Lachish. They worshiped a god
called Dagon, and set up his idol in the temple at Gaza. The idol of Dagon was a hide-
ous-looking creature with the head and arms
of a man and the body of a fish.

Not all the Israelites, however, succumbed
to idol worship. Some of the people remained
true and devout worshipers of the God of Is-

Gideon put the army to rout

rael. Among these was a man by the name of Manoah and his wife, who belonged to the tribe of Dan and who lived at Zorah. They were righteous and devout, but they had no child to bless their home.

At this time, an angel of the Lord appeared to Manoah's wife and said to her, "You are going to bear a son. Therefore be careful, and drink no wine or strong drink, and eat nothing unclean. When your son is born, he shall be dedicated to God by the Nazarite vow; and he shall in time begin to deliver Israel from the hand of the Philistines." Then Manoah's wife came and told her husband how the angel had appeared to her and given her the promise of a son. They were both very happy.

Then Manoah prayed earnestly to God and said, "O, my Lord, let the man of God whom you sent come again to us, and teach us what we are to do for the child who is going to be born to us." And God heard the prayer of Manoah, and the angel of God came again to his wife as she sat in the field alone. And she ran to tell her husband, "Behold, the man who appeared to me the other day has come again." And Manoah went with his wife, and came to the man and said to him, "Are you the man who spoke to my wife?" And he replied, "I am." And Manoah said, "Now when your promise is fulfilled, how shall we arrange the child's life, and what shall we do for him?" And the angel of the Lord said to Manoah, "Of all that I said to the woman let her take heed. She may not eat of anything that comes of the vine, neither let her drink wine or strong drink, or eat any unclean thing; all that I commanded her let her observe."

Then Manoah said to the angel of the Lord, "I pray you, let us detain you until we have prepared a kid for you." But the angel replied, "Even if you detain me I will not eat any of your food; if you prepare a burnt offering, you must offer it to the Lord." Manoah, not knowing that he was speaking to an angel of the Lord, inquired, "What is your name, so that, when your promise is fulfilled we may do you honor?" The angel of the Lord replied, "Why do you ask my name, seeing that it is a secret?"

So Manoah took the kid with the meat offering, and offered it upon a rock to the Lord; to the God who works wonders. And when the flame went up toward heaven from the altar, the angel of the Lord ascended in the flame as Manoah and his wife looked on; and they fell on their faces to the ground and worshiped.

But the angel of the Lord appeared no more to Manoah and his wife. Then Manoah knew that he was an angel of the Lord. And Manoah said to his wife, "We shall surely die, because we have seen God." But his wife said to him, "If the Lord had been pleased to kill us, he would not have accepted a burnt offering and a meal offering at our hands, or shown us all these things, or told us such things as these."

In due time the wife of Manoah gave birth to a son, and they called him Samson, which means "sunny" or "little sun." And the boy grew, and the Lord blessed him. Samson grew up to be an exceptionally strong and powerful young man. As he beheld how his people were oppressed by the Philistines, the Spirit of the Lord began to stir him in Mahaneh-dan, the place where the Danite spies had camped, between Zorah and Eshtaol. Thus Samson became aware of the mission to which God had called him: to deliver his people from the bondage of the Philistines.

The angel of the Lord ascended in the flame as Manoah and his wife looked on

Samson's Feats of Deliverance

Judges 14:1–16:3

THE secret of Samson's great strength lay in his vow to live close to God. As an outward sign of this Nazarite vow, Samson let his hair grow long and did not drink any wine or strong drink. He carried out the work God wanted him to do by performing a number of feats of strength to harass and punish the Philistines.

The first thing he did, in order to find an occasion against them, was to marry a daughter of the Philistines who lived at Timnath. His parents did not want him to marry a Philistine woman because they feared Samson might become a worshiper of Dagon. But they did not know the Lord was leading Samson to do this, so that he might have an opportunity to punish the Philistines.

Samson persuaded his father and mother to go with him to Timnath to see the woman he had chosen to become his wife. On this journey a young lion roared at him; and the Spirit of the Lord came mightily upon him, and he seized the jaws of the lion and tore him apart, and slew him with his bare hands. But he did not tell his father or mother what he had done. He went down and talked with the woman of Timnath, and she pleased Samson well.

Later he returned to Timnath to take her to be his wife; and he turned aside to see the carcass of the lion, and behold, there was a swarm of bees in the carcass of the lion, and honey. Samson took some of the honey in his hands, and went on his way, eating it. He gave some of the honey to his parents, and they ate it. But he did not tell them that he had taken the honey from a lion's carcass.

According to the custom of those times, Samson made a wedding feast at Timnath, and a large company of people attended the feast. Seeking some way to punish the Philistines, Samson proposed this riddle to the people:

"Out of the eater came forth meat,
  And out of the strong came forth sweetness."

Samson made a bargain with them that if they could solve the riddle within seven days, he would give them thirty sheets and thirty changes of clothing. If they could not solve the riddle, they were to give him the same number of garments. They tried for three days to guess the riddle, but could not. So they went to Samson's wife privately and threatened to punish her with fire if she did not entice him to explain the riddle. Samson's wife pouted and wept before him for several days until he finally explained the riddle. Then she explained it to her countrymen.

And the men of the city said to Samson on the seventh day before the sun went down,

"What is sweeter than honey?
  And what is stronger than a lion?"

Samson was very angry that he had been thus tricked by the Philistines. The Spirit of the Lord came upon him, and he went down

116

Samson slew the lion

to Ashkelon and slew thirty men; then he stripped them of their garments and gave them to those who had explained the riddle. Samson's anger was aroused, and he went back to his father's house. But Samson's wife was given to his companion, who had been his best man.

After a time, Samson went back to Timnath to visit his wife. But her father told him that she had been given to another man. Samson was furious at this insult, and said, "This time I will not be to blame for punishing the Philistines for the wrong they have done." So Samson went out and caught three hundred foxes, and tied their tails together, two by two, and put a torch between each pair of tails.

And when he had set fire to the torches, he let the foxes go into the standing grain of the Philistines, and burned up both the shocks and the standing grain, as well as the olive orchards.

The infuriated Philistines asked, "Who has done this?" They were told that Samson had done it because his father-in-law had given his wife to another man. In retaliation, the Philistines came up and burned the Timnite and his daughter with fire. And Samson said to them, "Since you have done this, I will be avenged upon you, and after that I will cease." And he assaulted them hip and thigh with a great slaughter; and then he went down and hid in the cave of the rock of Etam.

Then the Philistines came up and pitched camp in Judah, and made an attack on Lehi.

And the men of Judah said, "Why have you now come up against us?" They replied, "To bind Samson, and to do to him as he has done to us." Then three thousand men of Judah went down to the rock of Etam to bind Samson and turn him over to the Philistines.

They were willing to give up their champion and defender to save themselves from further trouble. Samson permitted himself to be bound by the men of Judah, after getting them to promise not to kill him themselves. So they bound him with two new ropes, and brought him up from Etam.

When Samson came to Lehi, the Philistines shouted against him. And the Spirit of the Lord same mightily upon him, and he broke the ropes about his arms as easily as if they had been strings. And he found a fresh jawbone of an ass, and seized it in his hand, and with it he slew a thousand of the Philistines.

Then, in his rough way, Samson sang,

"With the jawbone of an ass, heaps upon
    heaps,
With the jaw of an ass I have slain a thou-
    sand men."

When he had finished, he flung away the jawbone from his hand; and he called that place Ramath-lehi, which means "hill of the jawbone."

After this tremendous struggle, Samson was very thirsty, and he prayed to God and said, "You have given this great deliverance into the hand of your servant; and now shall I die of thirst, and fall into the hands of the heathens?" And God cracked open a hollow place that was at Lehi, and there came water from it; and when Samson had drunk, his spirit returned, and he revived. Therefore the place was called Enhakkore, which means "the well of him that called."

And Samson judged Israel in the days of the Philistines twenty years.

But Samson was not always true to his vow to live a clean life and to devote his great strength to the service of God. He brought shame upon himself by going down to the Philistine city of Gaza and associating there with a woman of bad reputation. The men of Gaza were informed that Samson was there, and they surrounded the place and lay in wait for him all night at the gate of the city. They held their peace all night, saying, "In the morning, when it is light, we shall kill him."

But Samson stayed only until midnight, when he arose and went forth and took the doors of the gate of the city, and the two posts, and went away with them, bar and all, and put them on his mighty shoulders, and carried them off to the top of a hill near Hebron. Thus Samson escaped with his life.

THIRTY-EIGHT

Samson's Betrayal and Death

Judges 16:4–31

SAMSON's weakness for falling in love with Philistine women finally brought about his downfall. The woman of Timnath and the woman of Gaza had already caused him a good deal of trouble and sorrow. But now he fell in love with a daughter of the Philistines in the valley of Sorek, a beautiful and heartless woman by the name of Delilah. She did not love Samson at all, but sought only to win his favor so that she might betray him to the rulers of her people.

When the lords of the Philistines learned that Samson was coming to court Delilah, they thought of a plan to overcome their hated enemy. They came to Delilah privately, and offered her a large sum of money, eleven hundred pieces of silver, if she would find out the secret of Samson's great strength, so that they might overwhelm him and bind him.

Delilah was perfectly willing to betray Samson for this large sum of money which she coveted very much. So when Samson next visited her, she said to him, "Tell me, I pray

you, the secret of your great strength, and how you might be bound by those who would subdue you." Samson, making a joke of the matter, and desiring to play another of his tricks, said to Delilah, "If they should bind me with seven green willow twigs which have not been dried, then I shall become weak and be an ordinary man." So she quickly procured seven green twigs from the Philistine lords, and bound Samson with them. In the meantime, she stationed men in an inner room to lie in wait, ready to pounce on Samson. Then she called out to him, "The Philistines are here to seize you, Samson." But Samson rose up and broke the green twigs, as a stalk of flax breaks when it touches the fire. So Delilah did not yet know the secret of his strength.

But Delilah wanted the money, and she tried again. Pouting before Samson in her womanly way, she chided him, saying, "Behold, you have mocked me, and told me lies; now tell me, I pray you, how you might be bound." Again in a mood of playful deception, Samson told her, "If they bind me fast with new ropes that have never been used, then I shall become weak and be like an ordinary man." So Delilah took new ropes and bound him with them, and again cried out, "The Philistines are here to take you, Samson." And the men were again lying in wait in an inner room. But the mighty Samson broke the ropes off his arms as though they were threads.

Delilah persisted in her efforts to entrap Samson, and said to him a third time, "Up to this time you have mocked me, and told me lies; tell me truly how you might be bound." Samson should have realized by now that Delilah meant to do him harm, but he foolishly kept up the game, saying this time, "If you weave the seven locks of my head with the web, then I shall become weak and be like an ordinary man." So while Samson was asleep, Delilah took the seven locks of his long hair, wove them into the web, and fastened them tight with the pin. Then she called to him, "The Philistines are about to pounce on you, Samson." But he awoke from his sleep, and rose up, and walked away with the pin of the beam and the web as easily as he had freed himself at other times.

Employing all of her womanly wiles, Delilah softened Samson further by saying that if he really loved her he would be willing to tell her the secret of his strength. And when she pressed him hard with her honeyed words day after day, and urged him, Samson became deeply vexed and troubled in his soul. Finally, in a moment of weakness, and against his better judgment, he told her everything that was in his heart, saying, "A razor has never been put to my head; for I have been a Nazarite to God from the day of my birth. If I am shaved, then my strength will go from me, and

I shall become weak and be like an ordinary man."

When the wicked Delilah saw that he had at last told her the truth, she sent for the lords of the Philistines saying, "Come up this once, for he has showed me all his heart." Then the conspirators came up to her, and brought the money they had promised her with them. Then when the heartless woman had lulled Samson to sleep upon her knees, she called a man and had him shave off the long flowing locks of Samson's hair. Then she began to vex him, and his strength went from him. Once more she cried out, "The Philistines are about to fall upon you, Samson." And Samson awoke from his fatal sleep and said, "I will go out as I have done before, and shake myself free." But alas! he did not know that, as a result of the betrayal of his vow, the Lord had departed from him. And the waiting Philistines fell upon Samson and put out his eyes, and brought him down to Gaza, and bound him with fetters of brass; and set him to grind at the mill of the prison.

The Philistines rejoiced greatly at having captured and conquered their hated enemy Samson. So the lords of the Philistines assembled at their temple to offer a great sacrifice to their god Dagon, and to rejoice; for they said, "Our god has delivered Samson our enemy into our hands." And when the people who were gathered together saw Samson in his pitiful plight, they praised their god and said, "Our god has delivered into our hands our enemy, the destroyer of our country, who has slain many of our people."

And when their hearts were merry, they said, "Bring Samson in, so that he may make sport for us." So they brought the blind Samson out of the prison, and he made sport for them in the court of the temple. And the people mocked and jeered and taunted Samson

Samson leaned against the pillars with all his might

as he groped about in his blindness like a clumsy beast of burden.

Presently Samson was made to stand between the pillars which supported the roof of the temple of Dagon. And Samson said to the lad who led him by the hand, "Let me feel the pillars upon which the house stands, so that I may lean against them." Now the house of Dagon was full of men and women; all the lords of the Philistines were there, and on the flat roof were about three thousand men and women, who were looking while Samson made sport for them.

Then Samson called upon the Lord and said, "O Lord God, remember me, I pray you, and strengthen me, I pray you, only this once, O God, so that I may be at once avenged upon the Philistines for my two eyes." And Samson took hold of the two middle pillars upon which the house stood, one with his right hand and the other with his left hand. And Samson

said, "Let me die with the Philistines." Then he leaned against the pillars with all his might; and they toppled, and the house fell upon the lords and upon all the people that were in it.

And so Samson perished with all of the Philistines. So it came to pass that the dead that Samson slew at his own death were more than he had slain during his life. Although blinded by his enemies, Samson renewed his vow to God, and God gave him the strength to perform his greatest work of deliverance against the Philistines.

Then the brothers of Samson and all the members of his family came down and took up the broken body of their dead hero. And they took him home and buried him in the tomb of Manoah his father, between Zorah and Eshtaol. And Samson, the strong man of the Hebrews, had judged the people of Israel for twenty years.

THIRTY-NINE

Ruth Chooses to Go With Naomi

Ruth 1:1–2:23

THE story of Ruth was written to show how this noble young woman from the heathen country of Moab became a worshiper of the God of Israel, and how she became an ancestress of David from whose lineage Jesus was born. It is one of the most beautiful stories in the world: of trouble and sorrow; of loyalty and devotion; of poverty and toil; of love and romance; of honor and preferment; of divine wisdom and providence.

In the days when the judges ruled there was a famine in the land of Israel. A certain man by the name of Elimelech who lived in Bethlehem decided to take his wife Naomi, and their two sons Mahlon and Chilion, and go to the land of Moab to escape the famine. So they went into the country of Moab and lived there for about ten years. But Elimelech died soon after they went to Moab, and Naomi was left with her two sons. These married Moabite women named Orpah and Ruth.

But Mahlon and Chilion too soon died, and Naomi was bereft of her husband and two sons.

The sorrowful Naomi decided that it was best for her to return to Bethlehem, for she had heard that food was plentiful there again. So she started on the journey to return to the land of Judah, her two daughters-in-law going with her. But Naomi tried to persuade Orpah and Ruth to go back to their parents' homes. She told them they would thus have a better opportunity to marry again and have their own homes. Both Orpah and Ruth wept greatly at the thought of parting from Naomi, whom they loved very much. Finally Orpah kissed her mother-in-law good bye and went back to her parents' house. But Ruth clung tightly to Naomi, and did not want to go back.

Naomi said to Ruth, "Behold, your sister-in-law has gone back to her people and to her gods; return after your sister-in-law." But Ruth made her memorable reply: "Entreat me not to leave thee, or to return from following after thee: for whither thou goest, I will go; and where thou lodgest, I will lodge: thy people shall be my people, and thy God my God:

"Where thou diest, will I die, and there will I be buried: the Lord do so to me, and more also, if aught but death part thee and me."

And when Naomi saw that Ruth was bent on going with her, she held her peace.

So the two women journeyed on until they came to Bethlehem. The whole town was moved by their plight, for the people had heard of the great sorrows and misfortunes that had come to Naomi. The women of Bethlehem said to her, "Can this be Naomi?" She said to them, "Do not call me Naomi, call me Mara; for the Almighty has dealt very bitterly with me. I went out full, and the Lord has brought me home again empty." So Naomi was not yet comforted in her sorrows.

Naomi and Ruth came to Bethlehem just at the beginning of the barley harvest. Now in Bethlehem there was a relative of Naomi's husband, a wealthy farmer by the name of Boaz. When Ruth volunteered to go and glean in the barley fields, in order to get some food for Naomi and herself, Naomi gave her permission; and Ruth went and gleaned in a certain field after the reapers. Although she did not know it, she happened to glean in a field that belonged to Boaz, who was Elimelech's relative.

And Boaz, the wealthy farmer of Bethlehem, came out to see how the harvest was progressing. He greeted his reapers, saying, "The Lord be with you." And they answered him, "The Lord bless you." Then Boaz, noticing a strange young woman gleaning in his fields, said to his servant in charge of the reapers, "Whose damsel is this?" The servant answered, "It is the Moabite damsel, who came back with Naomi from the country of Moab. She said to me, 'I pray you, let me glean and gather among the sheaves after the reapers.' So she came, and she has continued even from morning until now, without ever stopping to rest."

Then Boaz spoke to Ruth for the first time, saying, "Now listen to me, my daughter; do not go to glean in another field, or leave this one, but stay close to my maidens." Thus he spoke kindly to Ruth, offering to show her special favor. Then Ruth, bowing to the ground, said to Boaz, "Why have I found favor in your sight, that you should notice me, seeing that I am a stranger?"

Boaz answered Ruth, "I have been told about all that you have done on behalf of your mother-in-law since the death of your husband, how you left your father and mother

Ruth went and gleaned in a certain field

and the land of your birth and came to a people that you did not know before. May the Lord recompense you for all your good works, and a full reward be given you by the Lord God of Israel, under whose wings you have come to take shelter." Ruth humbly replied, "Let me find favor in your sight, my lord, for you have comforted me by speaking so kindly to me, though I am not one of your handmaidens."

Boaz also invited Ruth to eat with his reapers at mealtime, seeing that she had nothing of her own to eat. When she went forth to glean again, he privately instructed his reapers to pull out stalks of grain from their sheaves and leave them for Ruth to glean.

So Ruth gleaned in the field all day until evening. When she beat out what she had gleaned, she had about an ephah, or more than three pecks of barley. She took it home and showed Naomi what she had gleaned. Naomi asked, "Where have you gleaned today?" Ruth told Naomi that she had gleaned in the field of Boaz, and how kindly Boaz had spoken to her.

Then Naomi said to her daughter-in-law, "Blessed be he of the Lord, who has not stopped being kind to the living or to the dead." Then Naomi explained to Ruth, "The man is a member of our family, one of our nearest relatives." And she advised Ruth to continue to glean in the fields of Boaz. So Ruth continued to glean with the maidens of Boaz, until the end of the barley and wheat harvests. And Ruth lived with Naomi in Bethlehem, and they were happy to be together.

FORTY

Ruth Marries Boaz of Bethlehem

Ruth 3:1–4:22

THE story of how Ruth, the Rose of Moab, became the wife of Boaz, the wealthy farmer of Bethlehem, is one of charming romance, delicate beauty, steadfast loyalty, and unselfish love.

Of course Naomi thought it would be well for all concerned if Ruth could marry her husband's relative. So she planned as wisely as she could to bring this to pass. One day she said to Ruth, "My daughter, should I not seek a home for you, so that it may be well with you?" Then she reminded Ruth that Boaz was their relative, and that it would be well for her to cultivate his acquaintance. She suggested that Ruth put on her good clothes and pay a visit to Boaz at the threshing floor where he would be enjoying the harvest feast. She should observe where he slept, and should go in, and uncover his feet, and lie down at his feet; and Boaz would tell her what she should do. Ruth said to her mother-in-law, "All that you say to me I will do."

So Ruth went down to the threshing floor and did as Naomi had bidden her. When

Boaz had finished his eating and drinking that night, he went to lie down at the end of the heap of grain. Then Ruth came softly, and uncovered his feet, and lay down at his feet.

At midnight Boaz awoke and was startled to find a woman lying at his feet. He exclaimed, "Who are you?" And she answered, "I am Ruth, your handmaid; therefore spread your skirt over your handmaid; for you are a near relative."

Boaz, fully realizing the meaning of Ruth's noble gesture, said to her, "May the Lord bless you, my daughter; you have showed greater kindness now than at the beginning, in that you have not followed after young men, whether poor or rich." Then Boaz as-

sured Ruth that he would do the part of the relative as she desired. But he said there was another man, a nearer relative than Boaz, who must first be consulted.

In the morning, as Ruth was about to leave the threshing floor, Boaz gave her a present of six measures of barley to take to Naomi. When she came home, Naomi said to her, "How did you get along, my daughter?" Then Ruth told Naomi all that Boaz had done for her, and how he had sent the present of barley to her. Then Naomi advised Ruth, saying, "Wait, my daughter, until you learn what Boaz intends to do, for the man will not rest until he has settled the matter today."

According to his promise, Boaz promptly

Ruth softly approached the sleeping Boaz

arranged with the other relative to redeem the property of Elimelech, and at the same time to assume the obligation of becoming the husband of Ruth the Moabitess. The contract was sealed, according to the custom of the time, in the presence of the necessary witnesses. Then all the people who confirmed the transaction, and the elders, said, "We are witnesses. May the Lord make Ruth, who is coming into your house, like Rachel and like Leah, who together built up the house of Israel."

So Boaz of Bethlehem took Ruth the Moabitess as his wife in marriage. In due time the Lord blessed their happy home with the birth of a son. Then the women of Bethlehem said to Naomi, the happy grandmother, "Blessed be the Lord, who has not left you today without a kinsman; and may his name be famous in Israel! He shall be to you a restorer of your life, and a nourisher of your old age; for your daughter-in-law who loves you, who is better to you than seven sons, has borne him." Then Naomi took the child and laid him in her bosom and nurtured him. So Naomi was comforted and happy again.

The son of Ruth and Boaz was named Obed. Years later Obed became the father of Jesse, and Jesse became the father of David.

IV.

STORIES

ABOUT

THREE KINGS OF

UNITED ISRAEL

Saul Becomes Israel's First King

I Samuel 8:1–10:27

WHEN Samuel the prophet became too old to judge Israel any longer, and when his sons did not follow in his ways, the people asked Samuel to appoint a king to rule over them. They wanted to be governed, they said, like the other nations around them. Samuel was displeased at their request, and prayed to the Lord about it. But the Lord told Samuel to grant their wish, saying, "The people have not rejected you, but have rejected their God from reigning over them."

Samuel was instructed to warn the people of the difficulties and trials they might expect if a king were to rule over them. But they refused to heed Samuel's wise counsel, and demanded, "We will have a king over us; so that we also may be like all the nations, and that our king may judge us, and go out before us, and fight our battles." Then Samuel bade them return to their homes, saying that God would give them a king.

Samuel prayed that God would choose the right man to become Israel's first king. Soon God told Samuel that Saul was the man He had chosen.

This Saul was the son of Kish, a very rich man of the tribe of Benjamin. Saul was an excellent young man and very handsome. There was not among the children of Israel a man of more pleasing appearance than he; from his shoulders upward he was taller than any of his people.

Once some of the asses of Kish wandered away and were lost, and Kish sent Saul and one of his servants to find them. They searched in different places for several days, but could find no trace of the asses. Finally Saul said, "Come, let us return, lest my father stop caring about the asses and start worrying about us."

But the servant did not want to return until they had found the lost animals. So he suggested that they stop in the city near by and ask the man of God to tell them where they could find the asses. But Saul did not want to do this, because he said they had no present to give to the man of God. The servant said he had a piece of money they could give, so they went to the city to seek Samuel.

As they drew near the city gate, they came upon some maidens going out to a well to draw water. They asked the maidens, "Is the seer in the city?" They said that he was, and that they would find him at the high place where Samuel was about to bless the sacrificial feast prepared for the people. As they went up into the city, they beheld Samuel advancing toward them on his way to the high place. But they did not know that it was the man of God.

Now the day before the Lord had told Samuel, "Tomorrow about this time I will send you a man from the land of Benjamin, and you will anoint him to be king over my people Israel."

When Samuel saw Saul, the Lord said, "Behold the man of whom I spoke to you. He is

Samuel took a vial of oil and poured it on Saul's head

the one who shall reign over my people."

Then Saul went up to Samuel in the gate and said, "Tell me, I pray you, where the house of the seer is." Samuel answered Saul, "I am the seer; go up before me to the high place, for you shall eat with me today, and tomorrow I will let you go, and will tell you all that is in your heart."

Then Samuel told Saul not to worry any more about the lost asses, for they had been found. "And now," Samuel said to Saul, "you are the man for whom all Israel is looking." Saul was greatly surprised at this, and modestly replied, "I am a Benjaminite, of the smallest of the tribes of Israel. Why then do you say such a thing to me?"

Samuel took Saul and his servant with him to the feast, and gave them a place among the honored guests. Samuel arranged that the best of the food be set before Saul, and told him that it had been kept especially for him. After the feast was over, Samuel took Saul to a quiet place on the housetop, where he slept during the night.

Early the next morning Samuel awakened Saul and said that it was time for him to return to his father's house. Samuel walked with Saul to the edge of the city. There he said to Saul, "Send your servant on ahead, and stay here with me for a while, so that I may show you the word of God."

Then Samuel took a vial of oil and poured it on Saul's head, and kissed him and said, "The Lord has indeed anointed you to be ruler over his people Israel."

Samuel then gave three signs to Saul by which he would know that the Lord had chosen him to be king over Israel. Two men would meet him by Rachel's tomb who would tell him that his father's asses had been found, and that Kish was now worried about his son. Further on, three men would meet him and give him two loaves of bread, which he was to accept. Lastly, as he came to a certain city, he was to meet a band of prophets, join their company, and prophesy with them.

All these signs came to pass according to Samuel's word. The Spirit of God came upon Saul and he prophesied among the prophets at Gibeah. Later Samuel called all the people together at Mizpah, and presented Saul to them as their new king. And Samuel said to all the people, "Behold the man whom the Lord has chosen. There is none like him among all the people." And all the people shouted, "God save the king!"

Saul's Disobedience and Rejection as King

I Samuel 14:47–15:35

SAUL became a great warrior, and God helped him and his armies to win many victories over the Philistines and other enemies that troubled the Israelites. He fought against the Moabites, the Ammonites, and the Edomites and defeated them. He vanquished the Amalekites and delivered Israel out of the hands of those who sought to despoil them. Saul strengthened his army by adding to it all the strong, valiant young men he could find.

One day the old prophet Samuel sent for Saul and gave him this message: "The Lord sent me to anoint you king over his people Israel; now therefore listen to the words of the Lord. Thus says the Lord of hosts: 'I remember what Amalek did to Israel, how they lay in wait for them on the way when they came up out of Egypt. Now go and attack Amalek, and utterly destroy all that they have, and do not spare them; but slay both man and woman, infant and suckling, ox and sheep, camel and ass.' "

So Saul gathered his army of two hundred and ten thousand men and surrounded the city of Amalek. Before attacking, he sent word to the Kenites to depart from among the Amalekites, because they had showed kindness to Israel when they came up out of Egypt. Then Saul's soldiers fell upon the Amalekites and utterly defeated them with a great slaughter.

But Saul disobeyed the word of the Lord in that he took Agag, the king of the Amalekites, alive, and spared the best of the sheep, oxen, fatlings, and lambs, and all that was good. These spoils of victory Saul and his people took back with them for their own use.

Then the word of the Lord came to Samuel informing him of what Saul had done. God also said to Samuel, "I regret that I have set up Saul as king; for he has turned away from following me, and has not performed my commandments." Samuel was very indignant over Saul's disobedience, and cried out to the Lord all night in prayer.

And Samuel rose early in the morning and went to meet Saul as he returned with his secret spoils of war. Saul, seeking to hide his guilt, said to Samuel, "Blessed be you of the Lord; I have performed the commandment of the Lord." But Samuel was not deceived. He confronted Saul with the question, "What then is this bleating of sheep in my ears, and the lowing of oxen which I hear?"

But Saul, not willing to confess his own guilt, put the blame on the soldiers and the people, saying, "They have brought them from the Amalekites; for the people spared the best of the sheep and of the oxen to sacrifice to the Lord your God; and the rest we have utterly destroyed." Then Samuel said to Saul, "Enough! Now I will tell you what the

Lord has said to me tonight." Saul replied, "Say on."

And Samuel rebuked Saul, saying, "Even though you seem small in your own eyes, were you not made the head of the tribes of Israel? And did not the Lord anoint you king over Israel? The Lord sent you on a special errand, and said, 'Go and utterly destroy the sinners, the Amalekites, and fight against them until they are consumed.' Why then did you not obey the voice of the Lord, but pounced upon the spoil and did evil in the sight of the Lord?"

But Saul was not yet willing to admit his sin and disobedience, and again he tried to place the blame on the soldiers and the people for sparing the things that were supposed to be destroyed.

Then Samuel plainly told Saul that his disobedience had displeased the Lord, and further reprimanded him by saying, "Behold, to obey is better than sacrifice, and to heed is better than the fat of rams." Sadly Samuel pronounced the words of judgment: "Because you have rejected the word of the Lord, he has also rejected you from being king."

Then Saul admitted to Samuel that he had violated the commandment of the Lord because he feared the people and obeyed their wishes. Not yet was he willing to confess that

Saul grasped the skirt of Samuel's mantle and it tore

he had sinned by his own choice. He asked Samuel to pardon his sin, and return with him so that he might worship the Lord.

But Samuel said to Saul, "I will not return with you; for you have rejected the word of the Lord, and the Lord has rejected you from being king over Israel." As Samuel turned to go away, Saul grasped the skirt of his mantle and it tore. Then Samuel said to Saul, "The Lord has torn the kingdom of Israel from you today, and has given it to a neighbor of yours who is better than you."

Finally Saul repented and said, "I have sinned; yet honor me now, I pray you, before the elders of my people and before Israel, and turn again with me so that I may worship the Lord your God." So Samuel went back with Saul; and Saul worshiped the Lord.

Then Samuel went to the city of Ramah; and Saul went to his own house at Gibeah. And Samuel did not come again to see Saul until the day of his death, but Samuel suffered over Saul. And the Lord was sorry that he had made Saul king over Israel.

FORTY-THREE

Samuel Anoints David To Be King

I Samuel 16:1–13

FOR some time the prophet Samuel continued to suffer over King Saul because he had proved himself to be unworthy of ruling over God's chosen people. Perhaps Samuel took some of the blame for Saul's failure upon himself, for he had anointed Saul as Israel's first king. Then the word of the Lord came to Samuel, saying, "How long will you mourn for Saul, seeing that I have rejected him from reigning over Israel?" Samuel was comforted by hearing God speak to him again, for he knew that God would tell him what to do.

God directed Samuel, saying, "Fill your horn with oil, and go; I will send you to Jesse the Bethlehemite; for I have provided for a king among his sons." At first Samuel was

afraid to go, because he feared that Saul would hear of it and put him to death.

But the Lord said to Samuel, "Do not be afraid. Take a heifer with you and say, 'I have come to sacrifice to the Lord.' And call Jesse to the sacrifice, and I will show you what to do; and you shall anoint me one of the sons of Jesse whom I will name." So Samuel did what the Lord commanded, and came to Bethlehem.

The elders of the city came to meet Samuel with fear and trembling, because they feared they might have done something to displease the man of God. They asked Samuel, "Do you come in peace?" Samuel quieted their fears by replying, "I come in peace; I have come to sacrifice to the Lord. Now I

Samuel anointed David in the midst of his brothers

want you to sanctify yourselves, and come with me to the sacrifice." So Samuel sanctified Jesse and seven of his sons who were present, and called them to the feast.

So Jesse and seven of his sons came to the feast. Jesse had eight sons, but the youngest of them was away keeping the sheep. As the seven stalwart sons of Jesse stood before him, Samuel tried to pick out the one who should be anointed as Saul's successor. First he looked upon the oldest son Eliab, who was tall and strong and handsome. Samuel was impressed with Eliab's appearance, and said to himself, "Surely the Lord's anointed is before Him." But the Lord said to Samuel, "Do not look on his countenance, or on the height of his stature, because I have refused him. For the Lord does not see as man sees; for man looks on the outward appearance, but the Lord looks on the heart."

Then Jesse called his second son Abinadab, and had him pass before Samuel. And Samuel said, "The Lord has not chosen this one either." Then Jesse made his third son Shammah pass by. But Samuel's answer was the same, "The Lord has not chosen this one either." So Jesse had all seven of his sons pass by in turn before Samuel. And Samuel said to Jesse, "The Lord has not chosen these."

Then Samuel said to Jesse, "Are all of your sons here?" Jesse replied, "There still remains the youngest; but behold, he is out in the pasture fields keeping the sheep." Samuel then said to Jesse, "Send for him and have him brought to me; for we will not sit down to the feast until he comes."

So Jesse sent for his youngest son and brought him in before the prophet Samuel. Now this shepherd boy had a ruddy, healthy complexion and an altogether pleasing appearance. Immediately the Lord said to Samuel, "Arise, anoint him; for this is he."

Then Samuel took the horn of oil, and anointed David in the midst of his brothers to be Israel's future king. And the Spirit of the Lord came upon David from that day forward. After the feast was over, Samuel rose up and returned to Ramah.

David's Victory Over Goliath

I Samuel 17:1–58

During his reign, Saul fought many battles against the Philistines, the enemies of Israel. Now again the Philistines gathered their armies for battle at a place called Shochoh, overlooking the valley of Elah. Saul and the men of Israel gathered together in battle array on one side of the valley, and the army of the Philistines was drawn upon the other side.

The Philistines had a champion by the name of Goliath, who was a giant of a man nine feet nine inches tall. His huge body was entirely protected by heavy armor. He wore a brass helmet, and was armed with a very heavy coat of mail. His legs were covered with greaves of brass, and a spear of brass was slung between his shoulders. He carried a huge iron-pointed spear in his hand; and his shield-bearer went before him.

Goliath came forth from the camp of the Philistines and shouted this challenge to the armies of Israel: "Why have you come out to set your battle in array? Am I not a Philistine, and you servants of Saul? Choose a man for yourselves and let him come down to me. If he is able to fight with me and to kill me, then we will be your servants. But if I prevail against him and kill him, then you shall be our servants." Then the mighty warrior shouted, "I defy the armies of Israel today; give me a man, so that we may fight together." When Saul and his soldiers heard these words of the Philistine giant, they were dismayed and greatly afraid.

Now Jesse the Bethlehemite, the father of David, had sent his three oldest sons Eliab, Abinadab, and Shammah to join Saul's army. But David the youngest son stayed at home and divided his time between serving King Saul and caring for his father's sheep.

One day Jesse called David and asked him to take a supply of food to his brothers in Saul's army, and to find out how they were faring. So David rose early in the morning, left the sheep with a keeper, and took the provisions and went, as his father had commanded him. He carried a sack of parched grain and ten loaves of bread for his brothers, and a gift of ten cheeses for their captain.

David arrived at the encampment just as the soldiers were going forth to fight, shouting for the battle. David left the provisions with the keeper of the baggage, and ran into the ranks to greet his brothers. As he talked with them, behold, Goliath, the champion of the Philistines, came forth and shouted his defiant challenge again. And David heard it.

But the soldiers of Saul who saw and heard Goliath were filled with fear and fled from him. David inquired of the men who stood near him, "What shall be done for the man who kills this Philistine and takes away the reproach from Israel?" The people replied, "The man who kills this Philistine the king

139

will enrich with great riches, and will give him his daughter, and make his father's house free in Israel." David's spirit was moved, and he said, "Who is this Philistine that he should defy the armies of the living God?"

David's oldest brother Eliab heard him speak to the men, and he became very angry with David for talking so bravely. He scolded David for leaving the sheep in the wilderness and coming down just to see the battle. But David discreetly replied that he had done nothing wrong, and that he had merely asked a sensible question.

David's words were reported to Saul, and the king sent for him. David stood before Saul and said, "Let no man's heart fail because of him; your servant will go and fight with this Philistine." But Saul said to David, "You are not able to go against this Philistine to fight with him; for you are but a youth, and he a man of war from his youth." Then David told Saul how, in caring for his father's sheep, he had fought with the lion and the bear, and God had given him the strength to kill them. And David said, "The Lord who delivered me out of the paw of the lion, and out of the paw of the bear, will deliver me out of the hand of this Philistine."

Then Saul said to David, "Go and the Lord be with you." Then Saul gave David his own armor to try on: brass helmet, coat of mail, and great sword. But the armor was so heavy and cumbersome that David could hardly move. He said to Saul, "I cannot go with these; for I am not used to them." So he took them off. Then David took his shepherd staff in his hand, and chose five smooth stones from the brook and put them in his shepherd's bag, in his wallet; his sling was in his hand, and he drew near to the Philistine.

And the giant Philistine advanced toward David, with his shield-bearer before him. And when Goliath looked, and saw David, he disdained him; for he was but a youth, ruddy and healthy-looking. And the Philistine taunted David, saying, "Am I a dog, that you come to me with staves?" And the Philistine cursed David by his gods. Then the mighty warrior chided David, "Come to me, and I will give your flesh to the birds of the air and to the beasts of the field."

Then David answered the Philistine, "You come to me with a sword and with a spear and with a shield; but I come to you in the name of the Lord of hosts, the God of the armies of Israel, whom you have defied. Today the Lord will deliver you into my hand; and I will slay you, and take your head from you; and I will give the carcasses of the army of the Philistines today to the birds of the air and to the wild beasts of the earth; so that all the earth may know that there is a God in Israel. And all this assembly shall know that the Lord does not save with sword and spear; for the battle is the Lord's, and he will deliver you into our hands."

As the Philistine giant advanced to meet David, the shepherd lad ran quickly toward the army to meet the Philistine. And David put his hand in his bag and took out a stone, and slung it, and struck the Philistine on the forehead; the stone sank into his forehead and he fell on his face to the ground.

So David prevailed over the Philistine with a sling and with a stone, and struck the giant and killed him. But there was no sword in David's hand. So he ran to the fallen Philistine, and drew his great sword from its sheath, and cut off the giant's head with it. When the Philistine soldiers saw that their champion was dead, they fled in haste and disorder.

And the soldiers of Saul's army rose with

David slung a stone and struck the Philistine on the forehead

a shout and pursued the Philistines all the way back to their cities of Gath and Ekron. When they returned from chasing the Philistines, they despoiled the tents of the enemy which they had left behind.

And David took the head of Goliath as a trophy of his victory and brought it to Jerusalem. But he put the massive armor belonging to the dead Philistine giant into his tent.

And as David returned from the slaughter of the Philistine, Abner, the leader of Saul's army, took him and brought him before Saul with the head of the Philistine in his hand. And Saul said to David, "Whose son are you, young man?" And David replied, "I am the son of your servant Jesse, the Bethlehemite."

FORTY-FIVE

Saul Becomes David's Enemy

I Samuel 18:1–30

PRINCE Jonathan was present when David returned from his victory over Goliath and talked with King Saul. David and Jonathan immediately became friends, and Jonathan loved David as his own soul. Because of his great love for David, Jonathan made a covenant of friendship with him, and presented his own princely robe and the armor which he wore to his new-found friend. Saul kept David in his service from then on, and would not let him return to his father's house. David behaved well wherever Saul sent him; so that Saul set him over the men of war. David became very popular in the sight of the people, and also with Saul's servants.

As the victorious soldiers were coming home, after David's contest with the Philistine, the women came out of all the cities of Israel to meet King Saul, singing and dancing and playing instruments of music. And the women shouted to one another in the midst of the merrymaking:

"Saul has slain his thousands,
And David his ten thousands."

This made Saul very angry, and he was filled with envy toward David because they praised David more than the king himself. And Saul looked on David with suspicion and envy from that time on.

The next day David was playing the harp to comfort and soothe King Saul, as he did from time to time. Suddenly the evil spirit came upon Saul, and he stormed about the house with a spear in his hand. And in a fit of anger he turned and threw the spear at David, in an effort to kill him. But David dodged Saul's spear twice.

Saul believed that the Lord was with David, which made him all the more afraid of him. So Saul had David taken away from him, and

In a fit of anger Saul threw the spear at David

made a commander of a thousand soldiers. The Lord was with David, and he was successful in everything he did. When Saul saw this, he was afraid of David. But all the people of Israel loved David, as he went in and out among them.

Then Saul contrived a plot to get rid of David by having the Philistines kill him. He told David he would give his elder daughter Merab to become David's wife if he would go and fight the Philistines. But when the time came, Saul broke his promise and gave Merab for a wife to another man.

Saul had another daughter, Michal, who loved David. This pleased Saul, and again he offered to make David his son-in-law. David tried to excuse himself by saying that he was too poor and humble for such an honor. But Saul instructed his servants to tell David that the only marriage present he would require would be proof that David had killed a hundred Philistines. Thus Saul hoped to have David slain by the Philistines.

It pleased David well to think of becoming the king's son-in-law. So David went forth with his company of soldiers and killed two hundred of the Philistines, and reported the number to the king. Whereupon Saul gave his daughter Michal to David for a wife.

But as Saul became more and more convinced that the Lord was with David, and no longer with himself, he felt still more afraid of David. And as he saw how all Israel loved David, he became more and more filled with jealousy and envy. So Saul became a bitter enemy toward David continually.

From time to time the princes of the Philistines came out to fight the Israelites, and every time they came out David gained greater victories over them than all the servants of Saul. So David became highly regarded as a valiant commander among the men of Israel.

Jonathan Befriends David

I Samuel 19:1–20:42

KING Saul grew so envious and hateful toward David that he spoke openly to his son Jonathan and to all his servants about killing David. But Jonathan loved David greatly as his friend, and went at once to warn David of Saul's evil intention.

He told David that Saul sought to kill him, and advised him to hide himself in some secret place. Jonathan volunteered to speak to Saul on David's behalf, and then to let him know about the outcome.

So Jonathan went to his father, and spoke well of David, saying, "Let the king not sin against his servant David, because he has not sinned against you, and because his works have been of good use to you: for he took his life in his hands and slew the Philistine, and the Lord wrought a great salvation for all Israel. You saw it and rejoiced. Why then do you want to sin against innocent blood by killing David without cause?" Saul listened to this noble plea of his son on behalf of his friend David, and declared that he would not put David to death. Whereupon Jonathan called David and told him all these things. He also brought David to Saul, and David remained in Saul's presence as in the past.

There was war again with the Philistines, and David went forth with his soldiers and fought a victorious battle against them. As a result, David's popularity increased and Saul's enmity toward David revived. As David was playing the harp before Saul in his house, the evil spirit came upon Saul and he sought to pin David to the wall with his spear. But David dodged Saul, as he had once before, and the spear stuck in the wall. David fled out of the house and went to his own home.

Saul sent messengers to watch David's house that night and to kill him in the morning. But Michal, David's wife, told him about the watchers and warned David, "If you do not save your life tonight, tomorrow you will be killed." So Michal let David down through a window, and he escaped without the guards seeing him.

Then Michal stuffed an image with a head of goat's hair and covered it on David's bed. And when Saul sent messengers to take David, she told them that David was sick. But Saul ordered his servants to bring David to him in the bed, so that he might put him to death. The servants obeyed, and carried the bed with its stuffed image to Saul. When Saul discovered the ruse, he was very angry, and said to Michal, "Why have you deceived me thus, and helped my enemy escape?" To spare herself, Michal falsely stated that David had threatened to kill her if she did not help him to escape.

Having once more eluded the evil designs of Saul, David fled to Samuel at Ramah, and told the man of God his troubles. Samuel took David with him to Naioth. When Saul learned of this, he sent messengers to capture David. But when they came and saw Samuel and the company of prophets worshiping God and prophesying, they were moved by the Spirit of God to worship with them. The same thing happened to a second group of messengers, and a third.

Finally Saul himself went to Ramah and inquired for Samuel and David. When Saul found Samuel engaged in worship and the teaching of God's word, he, too, was moved by the Spirit of God to prophesy before Samuel. That is why the saying arose: "Is Saul also among the prophets?"

But David feared Saul, and fled from Naioth in Ramah and came and sought out his friend Jonathan. David said to Jonathan, "What have I done? What is my offense? And what is my sin before your father, that he seeks my life?" Jonathan assured David that he would not die, and promised to keep him informed concerning Saul's plans. But David was not fully comforted, and sadly lamented, "Truly, there is but a step between me and death." Then Jonathan said to David, "Whatever you desire, I will do for you."

Then David proposed a plan to test Saul's attitude toward him, whether for good or evil. David was to remain absent from one of Saul's feasts, and hide himself in the field for three days. If Saul inquired for David, Jonathan was to say that David had gone to Bethlehem to keep the feast with his family. If Saul approved, David was to rest easy. But if Saul became angry, then David was to know that the king meant evil against him. Then they arranged a plan by which Jonathan would tell David about Saul's intentions.

They went out into the field and devised a clever signal by which Jonathan could forewarn David if the king determined to kill him. Jonathan was to pretend to shoot arrows at a mark, close to where David was to be in hiding, and by a prearranged signal was to inform David whether to stay or to flee.

The day of the feast came, and the king sat down in his accustomed place to eat food. Jonathan sat opposite, and Abner sat at Saul's side, but David's place was empty.

Saul noticed David's absence, but said nothing the first day. On the second day, when David's place was still empty, he said to Jonathan, "Why has the son of Jesse not come to my table either yesterday or today?" Then Jonathan explained to Saul that he had given David leave to join his family at Bethlehem.

Then Saul became furiously angry at his own son, and cursed him for befriending David. He commanded Jonathan to go and bring David to him so that he might put him to death. Jonathan answered Saul his father, "Why should David be put to death? What has he done?" But Saul in a rage threw his spear at Jonathan. So Jonathan knew that his father was determined to kill David. And Jonathan arose from the table in fierce anger and refused to eat anything. He was grieved for his friend David because of his father's cruel attitude.

In the morning Jonathan went out into the field to keep his appointment with David. He took with him his bow and arrows, and a little boy to watch him shoot the arrows. Jonathan said to the little boy, "Run, go find the arrows which I shoot." As the boy ran, he shot an arrow beyond him. And when the boy came to the place where the arrow was shot, Jonathan shouted after him and said, "Is not the arrow beyond you?" And Jonathan shouted after the boy, "Speed away, make haste, do not wait!"

So the boy gathered up the arrows and brought them to Jonathan. But he did not know the meaning of what he had done; only Jonathan and David knew. Jonathan gave the bow and arrows to the boy and told him to carry them back to the city.

As the boy ran, Jonathan shot an arrow beyond him

As soon as the boy had gone, David got up from the place where he had been hiding and came to Jonathan. The two friends embraced and kissed one another, and wept with one another until David could scarcely stop. Then Jonathan said to his dear friend David, "Go in peace, since we have both sworn in the name of the Lord, saying, 'May the Lord be between me and you, and between my offspring and your offspring forever.'" And David rose and departed, and Jonathan returned to the city.

FORTY-SEVEN

David Spares Saul at Engedi

I Samuel 24:1–22

SO DAVID was separated from his friend Jonathan, and forced to flee from the presence of King Saul. There followed a long and difficult period of trial and trouble in the life of David. He was pursued from one hiding-place to another by Saul and his soldiers, and hunted "like one hunts a partridge in the mountains." David fled from Saul to Nob, and from there to Achish. He departed from Achish and escaped to the cave of Adullam; and from there he went to Mizpeh and to Keilah. He took refuge in the wilderness of Ziph, and later in the wilderness of Maon.

While Saul was hunting David in the wilderness of Maon, the Philistines made a raid in the land of Israel, and Saul was compelled to stop pursuing David to go back and fight the Philistines. Then David went up from Maon, and took shelter in the strongholds of Engedi, a wild and mountainous section on the western shore of the Dead Sea.

When Saul returned from fighting the Philistines, he was told that David had fled to the wilderness of Engedi. Then Saul took three thousand chosen men from his army, and went to seek David and his men upon the rocks of the wild goats. And Saul came to the sheepfolds by the way, where there was a large cave. Being weary with his journey, he entered into the cave to rest awhile. In the shade and coolness of the cave, he soon fell fast asleep. Saul did not know that David and his men were hiding in the inmost corners of that very cave!

David's rough men wanted to pounce on the sleeping king and put him to death. They whispered to David, "The day has come of which the Lord said to you, 'Behold, I will deliver your enemy into your hand, so that you may deal with him as you please.'" But David restrained his men.

Instead David crept forward and with his sword stealthily cut off the skirt of Saul's robe. After he had done this, David felt ashamed at having lifted his hand against his king even in that harmless way. He said to his men, "The Lord forbids me to do this thing to my master, the Lord's anointed, to stretch forth my hand against him, seeing he is the anointed of the Lord." So David held his men back with these words, and did not let them attack Saul.

Completely unaware of how his life had been spared, Saul awoke from his nap, rose up and left the cave, and went on his way.

Then David also arose, and went out of the cave, and shouted after Saul, "My lord the king." Saul was surprised and startled to hear David's voice. And when he turned and looked behind him, David knelt on the ground and bowed his face to the earth in an attitude of obeisance. And David said to Saul, "Why do you heed the words of those who say, 'Behold, David seeks to hurt you'? Behold, today your eyes have seen how the Lord delivered you into my hands in the cave; and some bade me kill you, but I spared you. I said, 'I will not put forth my hand against my lord; for he is the Lord's anointed.'"

Holding up the piece of Saul's robe, David continued, "See, my father, see the skirt of your robe in my hand; for by the fact that I cut off the skirt of your robe, and did not kill

David stealthily cut off the skirt of Saul's robe

you, you can see for yourself that there is neither evil nor disloyalty in my heart. I have not sinned against you, yet you hunt my soul to take it. Let the Lord judge between me and you, and let the Lord avenge me of you; but my own hand shall not be upon you."

David went on to remind Saul how the Lord was protecting his servant David by saying, "After whom has the king of Israel come out? Whom are you pursuing? A dead dog! A flea! Let the Lord therefore be judge, and judge between you and me, and see, and plead my cause, and deliver me from your hand." Thus David spoke of the folly and futility of Saul's efforts to do him harm when the Lord was watching over him.

When David had finished speaking these words to Saul, the king replied, "Is this your voice, my son David?" And Saul wept loudly. Then he said to David, "You are more righteous than I; for you have rewarded me with good, whereas I have rewarded you with evil. And you have showed today how well you have dealt with me, inasmuch as when the Lord delivered me into your hands you did not kill me. For if a man finds his enemy, will he let him go away unharmed? For this reason may the Lord reward you with good for what you have done to me today."

Continuing to speak in this humble and penitent mood, Saul made a request of David, saying, "Behold, I know well that you shall surely be king, and that the kingdom of Israel shall be established in your hand. Therefore swear to me now by the Lord that you will not cut off my heritage after me, and that you will not destroy my name out of my father's house."

David readily agreed to keep this promise to Saul. Thus he showed his willingness to forgive Saul for all the evil and wrong he had plotted against him. David's true greatness appears in his gracious and magnanimous conduct toward King Saul, whom he regarded as the Lord's anointed.

After this interview, Saul left and returned to his home. But David took his men and went up to the safety of his mountain stronghold.

David Becomes King of Judah and Israel

II Samuel 1:26–6:19

AFTER King Saul and his sons had been slain by the Philistines in the battle of Mount Gilboa, David lamented with great sorrow over Saul and Jonathan for many days. He composed a beautiful eulogy for his friend Jonathan, in which he said, "I am distressed for you, my brother Jonathan; very pleasant have you been to me; your love to me was wonderful, surpassing the love of women. How the mighty are fallen, and the weapons of war perished!"

After this David inquired of the Lord, "Shall I go up into any of the cities of Judah?" And the Lord directed David to go up to the city of Hebron. So David took his family, and the men who were with him and their families, and went up to dwell at Hebron. There the men of Judah came to him and anointed David king over the house of Judah.

A number of years passed during which there was a long war between the house of Saul and the house of David. But David grew in power and influence, while the house of Saul became weaker and weaker.

In due time all the tribes of Israel came to David at Hebron and said, "Behold, we are your flesh and bone. Also in time past, when Saul was king over us, you were the one who led out and brought in Israel; and the Lord said to you, 'You shall feed my people Israel, and you shall be ruler over Israel.'" So all the elders of Israel came to the king at Hebron; and King David made a covenant with them at Hebron before the Lord, and they anointed David king over Israel. David was thirty years old when he began to reign, and he reigned forty years. At Hebron he reigned over Judah seven years and six months; and at Jerusalem he reigned over all Israel and Judah thirty-three years.

David established his united kingdom in the city of Jerusalem. First he had to conquer and drive out the Jebusites, a hostile people who had inhabited the region since the time of Joshua. In spite of stubborn resistance, David took the stronghold of Zion, which was afterward called the city of David. The king lived in the stronghold and built up and fortified the city round about. And David grew more and more powerful; for the Lord, the God of hosts, was with him.

With the generous assistance of Hiram king of Tyre, who furnished cedar trees, carpenters, and masons, David built his royal palace upon Mount Zion, within the walled city. And David perceived that the Lord had established him king over Israel, and that He had exalted his kingdom for the sake of His people Israel.

The Philistines, who occupied certain sections of the land of Israel, were displeased when they learned that David had been made king over all Israel. So at two different times they gathered their armies in a valley near Jerusalem and tried to capture the city. But both times David and his soldiers defeated them, because they fought the battles as the Lord commanded David to do. The Philistines did

David lamented with great sorrow over Saul and Jonathan for many days

not attack Israel again while David was king.

Some time later, David remembered that the ark of the Lord was still at Kirjath-jearim, where it had been for twenty years, ever since it had been captured and returned by the Philistines. So he called all the people of Israel together and they went to bring back the ark of the Lord to Jerusalem.

After several mishaps and frightening ex- periences, the ark was finally brought to Je- rusalem and housed in a tabernacle that David had prepared to receive it. The people celebrated its safe return with music and dancing and rejoicing. Sacrifices were offered to the God of Israel, and David blessed the people in the name of the Lord of hosts, and provided generous servings of food to all the people for a great feast of thanksgiving.

FORTY-NINE

Solomon Succeeds David as King

I Kings 1:1–2:12

THE years went by, and David became old and infirm, no longer able to serve the people as their king. Then David's son Adonijah exalted him- self and declared that he would become king in his father's place. He prepared for himself chariots and horsemen, and fifty young men to run before him as he rode through the streets of Jerusalem. He enlisted the aid of Joab the captain of David's army, and of Abiathar the high priest. Then he made a great feast in a valley outside the walls of Je- rusalem, to which he invited Joab and Abia- thar, all his brothers, and all the royal officials of Judah. But he did not invite Nathan the prophet, or Benaiah the captain of David's bodyguard, or Solomon his brother.

Nathan, the prophet of God, was troubled by Adonijah's plot to seize the throne. He knew that God had chosen Solomon to suc- ceed his father David, and he feared that

David did not know about Adonijah's plan to take the throne instead of Solomon. So Na- than went to Bathsheba, Solomon's mother, and told her of Adonijah's evil plot to displace her son. He reminded her of David's promise to her that Solomon should reign on David's throne after him.

So Bathsheba hastened to David's room and to the bedside where the aged king was being cared for by his Shunamite nurse. Bath- sheba bowed and did obeisance to the king, and David said, "What do you wish?"

Bathsheba replied, "My lord, you swore to your handmaiden by the Lord your God, say- ing, 'Assuredly Solomon your son shall reign after me, and he shall sit upon my throne.'" Then she proceeded to tell David of Adon- ijah's plot to take the kingdom away from Solomon.

At this point, according to a prearranged plan, Nathan the prophet came before the king and confirmed the word of Bathsheba. Then Nathan said to David, "Has this thing been done by my lord the king, and you have not revealed it to your servant, who should sit on the throne of my lord the king after him?" Then King David answered, "Call Bathsheba to me." And Bathsheba came and stood before the king. And the king reaffirmed his covenant, saying, "As the Lord lives who has redeemed my soul out of all distress, just as I swore to you by the Lord God of Israel, saying, 'Solomon your son shall reign after me, and he shall sit upon my throne in my stead,' just so will I certainly do today." Then Bathsheba bowed with her face to the ground, and did obeisance to the king, and said, "Let my lord King David live forever!"

David acted at once and called Zadok the priest, Nathan the prophet, and Benaiah the son of Jehoiada before him. Then the king instructed them what to do, saying, "Take with you the servants of your lord, and have Solomon my son ride upon my own mule, and bring him down to Gihon. There let Zadok the priest and Nathan the prophet anoint him king over Israel; and blow the trumpet and say, 'God save King Solomon.' Then you come up after him, so that he may come and sit upon my throne; for he shall be king in my stead; and I have appointed him to be ruler over Israel and over Judah." And Benaiah answered the king, "Amen. Let the Lord God of my lord the king say so too. As the Lord has been with my lord the king, even so may he be with Solomon and make his throne greater than the throne of my lord King David."

King David's orders were quickly obeyed. Zadok, Nathan, and Benaiah, together with many people of the city, went down and brought Solomon to Gihon riding on King David's mule. There Zadok the priest took a horn of oil from the tabernacle and anointed Solomon. Then they blew the trumpet; and all the people said, "God save King Solomon." And all the people went up after him, playing pipes and rejoicing with great joy, so that the earth resounded with the noise.

The sound of their rejoicing was heard in the valley where Adonijah and his friends were having their feast. When Joab heard the sound of the trumpet, he said, "What is the meaning of this tumult in the city?" While he was speaking, a messenger came to tell the company that David had made Solomon king, and that Solomon now sat upon the royal throne.

Adonijah was filled with fear when he heard that his father had made Solomon king of Israel. His guests were also afraid, and hastily left the scene of their feasting and returned to their homes. Adonijah feared what Solomon might do to him, and for protection he ran to the tabernacle and caught hold of the horns of the altar, saying, "Let King Solomon swear to me today that he will not slay his servant with the sword."

When King Solomon heard what his brother Adonijah had done, he promised to deal kindly with him. So Adonijah came away from the altar and bowed before King Solomon. And the king permitted him to go to his house in safety and peace.

A short time after these events, David died and was buried in Jerusalem, which is called the city of David. And the period of time that David reigned over Israel was forty years; he reigned seven years in Hebron and thirty-three years in Jerusalem. So Solomon sat upon the throne of David his father; and his kingdom was solidly established.

Adonijah bowed before King Solomon

Solomon Prays for Wisdom and Understanding

I Kings 3:1–28

SOLOMON's reign began well, because he sought God's favor and blessing in all that he did. Solomon loved the Lord and sought to obey God's commandments as his father David had done before him. But because no house had yet been built for the name of the Lord, Solomon and the people were offering sacrifices and burning incense at certain high places.

Soon after he became king, Solomon went to the great high place at Gibeon, and offered a thousand burnt offerings to God upon the great altar which stood there. That night when Solomon lay down to sleep at Gibeon the Lord appeared to him in a dream. And God said to His servant, "Ask what I shall give you."

Then Solomon said to the Lord, "You showed your servant David my father great kindness because he walked before you in truth and in righteousness and in uprightness of heart; and you kept for him this great kindness, and gave him a son to sit on his throne. And now, O Lord my God, you have made your servant king instead of David my father; and I am but a little child: I do not know how to go out or come in. And your servant is in the midst of your people whom you have chosen, a great people, that cannot be numbered or counted for multitude. Give your servant therefore an understanding heart to judge your people, so that I may discern between good and bad: for who is able to judge this your so great a people?"

It pleased the Lord that Solomon had prayed in this humble and earnest fashion. God heard Solomon's prayer and said to him, "Because you have asked this thing, and have not asked for long life for yourself, or asked for riches or the life of your enemies, but have asked for understanding to discern between good and bad, behold, I will do according to your words: lo, I will give you a wise and understanding heart, so that there will have been none like you before you and there shall arise none like you after you. And I will also give you the things which you did not ask for: both riches and honor, so that there will not be any among the kings like you all your life. And if you walk in my ways, and keep my statutes and my commandments, as your father David did, then I will lengthen your days."

When Solomon awoke, he knew that the Lord had spoken to him in a dream. Then he arose and went back to Jerusalem and stood before the ark of the covenant of the Lord. He offered up burnt offerings and peace offerings to God, and made a great feast for all his servants.

Very soon King Solomon had a special opportunity to make use of the wisdom and un-

Solomon said, "Divide the living child in two, and give half to the one and half to the other"

derstanding which God had promised him. Two women came before the king, each the mother of a newborn baby, and asked the king to judge their case.

One of the women told this story. She said, "This woman and I live in the same house; and I gave birth to a child when she was living there. Three days later this woman also bore a child, and we were alone in the house. And this woman's child died in the night, because she lay on it. And she arose at midnight, and took my son from beside me while I was asleep, and laid it in her bosom, and laid her dead child in my bosom. And when I arose in the morning to nurse my child, behold, it was dead; but when I examined it closely in the morning, behold, it was not my son that I had borne."

But the other woman told a different story. She said to the first woman, "No, the living child is my son and the dead child is your son." But the first woman said, "No, the dead child is your son and the living child is my son." Thus they spoke before King Solomon.

Then the king said to the disputing women, "One of you says, 'This is my son that lives and your son is dead'; and the other says, 'No; but your son is dead, and my son is the one that is alive.'" And the king said to one of his servants, "Bring me a sword." And a sword was brought before the king. And Solomon said, "Divide the living child in two, and give half to the one and half to the other."

Then the woman to whom the living child belonged said to the king, for she yearned for her child, "Oh, my lord, give her the living child and in no way harm it."

But the deceitful woman whose child was dead said, "Let it be neither mine nor yours; divide it."

Then wise King Solomon answered and said, "Give the living child to the first woman and in no way harm it; she is the child's mother."

And all the people of Israel heard of the judgment which the king had given; and they feared the king; for they saw that the wisdom of God was in him, to do justice.

Solomon Builds the Temple of God

I Kings 5:1–8:66

IN the fourth year of his reign Solomon began to build the temple of the Lord on Mount Moriah. When David was king, he planned to build such a temple, but God did not permit him to carry out his purpose. The Lord had said to David, "You have been a man of war, and you cannot build a house for my presence to dwell in. But your son Solomon, whom I will set upon your throne in your place, shall build the house for my name."

Solomon wrote a letter to Hiram, the king of Tyre, requesting that cedar trees from the mountains of Lebanon be cut to provide timber for the temple. Solomon offered to buy these trees and to send his servants to assist Hiram's men in felling them. Hiram had been a good friend of King David, and he rejoiced to hear that David's son was planning to build a house of the Lord. So he readily agreed to provide all of the cedar and fir timber that Solomon would need. Hiram's men cut the trees, took them from Lebanon to the sea, made them into rafts, and floated them down the coast to a port near Jerusalem. Solomon in turn supplied Hiram with great quantities of wheat and oil to feed his people.

King Solomon sent thirty thousand men to Lebanon, in relays of ten thousand a month, to help with the work of preparing the timber. Solomon also had seventy thousand burden-bearers and eighty thousand hewers of stone at work in mountains, besides three thousand three hundred chief officers in charge of this work. At Solomon's command, they dug out huge stones, costly stones, with which to lay the foundation of the house.

The timbers and the stones were so prepared and so fashioned that they could be put together in their proper places without the use of nails or hammers. So vast was the undertaking that thousands of men worked on it for seven years before it was completed.

When the great temple was finished, Solomon called an assembly of all the people of Israel, from every part of the kingdom, to participate in its dedication. The ark of the Lord was brought from Mount Zion to be placed in the inner sanctum of the temple. King Solomon and the congregation of Israel offered many sacrifices of sheep and oxen to the Lord. Then the priests carried the ark of the Lord into the most holy place, the inner sanctum of the temple. And when the priests came out of the holy place, a bright cloud appeared and the glory of the Lord filled the house of the Lord.

Then King Solomon turned, and blessed all the congregation of Israel, and addressed the people, saying, "Blessed be the Lord, the God of Israel, who spoke with his mouth to David my father, and with his hand has fulfilled what he promised." Then he made mention of the covenant God had made with the Chosen People when He brought them out of the land of Egypt, and which He had fulfilled even to that day.

King Solomon then led the people in a

Solomon led the people in a prayer of dedication before the altar of the Lord

prayer of dedication as he stood before the altar of the Lord. He worshiped God as the Creator of the heaven and the earth, whose glory and power and dominion could not be confined to a temple built with hands. He prayed that God's blessing would always rest upon the temple that had been built in His name, and asked God to listen to the prayers of those who prayed for forgiveness in His house, even foreigners from strange lands.

When Solomon had ended his prayer, the people again offered sacrifices before the Lord. Then, after a season of feasting, Solomon sent the people away; and they blessed the king, and returned to their tents joyful and glad of heart for all the goodness that the Lord had shown to David his servant and to Israel his people.

FIFTY-TWO

The Queen of Sheba Visits Solomon

I Kings 10:1–26

As time went on, King Solomon surpassed all the kings of the earth in riches and in wisdom. And all the earth sought out Solomon to hear his wisdom which God had put in his heart. And those who came to visit Solomon and behold the glory of his kingdom brought rich presents of silver and gold, garments, spices, armor, horses, and mules, in great abundance year by year.

After the temple of the Lord had been completed, Solomon built a splendid palace for himself and another for his wife, the daughter of the ruler of Egypt. Altogether it took Solomon about twenty years to build the temple and these palaces.

Solomon also built many walled store cities in the mountains of Lebanon and in other parts of his dominion. And he built cities for his chariots and horsemen in the desert regions. He built up a large army to defend his kingdom against possible enemies. And he built a fleet of ships at Ezion-geber on the Red Sea. These ships sailed around Arabia to the land of Ophir, from whence they brought great quantities of gold.

Jerusalem itself became a city of riches and splendor. Besides the wonderful temple and the magnificent palace of King Solomon, there were many streets with beautiful houses. In the pleasant gardens exotic flowers bloomed, gorgeous peacocks strutted, and chattering monkeys scampered among the palm trees.

Within his palace the king had built a great ivory throne and overlaid it with the finest gold. The throne had six steps, and the back of the throne was rounded on top; there were arm rests on either side of the seat, and two lions stood beside the arm rests. Also twelve lions stood there, one on either end of each of the six steps. There was not the like of it in any kingdom.

One of the royal monarchs who came to visit King Solomon was the queen of Sheba. Her homeland was a fabulous country in southwestern Arabia. The Sabeans were a commercial people, and traded with other countries in gold, spices, and precious stones. The queen of Sheba had heard of the fame of Solomon as a wise king and servant of God, and she came to put his wisdom to the test with difficult questions.

She came to Jerusalem with a very great train of attendants, and with camels bearing spices, and very much gold, and precious stones. And when she came before King Solomon she talked with him about all the matters that were in her heart. And Solomon was able to answer all her questions. There was nothing hidden from the king which he did not interpret for her.

And when the queen of Sheba had seen for herself all the wisdom of Solomon, the magnificent palace he had built, the sumptuous food of his table, the seating of his officials and the attendance of his servants and cupbearers, their elegant apparel, and the mag-

The Queen of Sheba came to visit King Solomon

nitude of the burnt offerings which he offered at the temple of God, her spirit was quite overwhelmed within her.

Then she said to King Solomon, "It was a true report that I heard in my own land of your affairs and of your wisdom. But I did not believe what I heard until I came and saw it with my own eyes. Behold, the half was not told me; your wisdom and prosperity far exceed the rumors which I heard."

Then she spoke with deep feeling to the king, saying, "Happy are your men. Happy are these your servants, who continually stand before you and hear your wisdom. Blessed be the Lord your God, who has delighted in you and set you on the throne of Israel. Because the Lord loved Israel forever, therefore he made you king, so that you might judge and do justice." Then she gave King Solomon a hundred and twenty talents of gold, and a very large gift of spices and precious stones; never again came such an abundance of spices as these which the queen of Sheba gave to King Solomon.

And King Solomon gave to the queen of Sheba all that she desired, whatever she asked besides what Solomon gave her of the royal bounty. When her memorable visit to the court of King Solomon came to an end, she went back to her own country.

V.

STORIES

ABOUT THE

DIVIDED

KINGDOM

How Elijah Was Fed During Famine

I Kings 17:1–24

ELIJAH was one of the greatest of the Old Testament prophets. His name means "my God is Jehovah," and he is sometimes known as "the prophet of fire." He was born at Tishbe in Gilead, and he was called "Elijah the Tishbite." He began his great work during the reign of Ahab, king of Israel, who ruled for twenty-two years from 874 to 852 B.C. Ahab was an exceedingly wicked king. He married Jezebel, a heathen woman of Tyre, and together they introduced the worship of the Tyrian god Baal into Israel. Their object was to destroy the worship of the true God of Israel. Elijah was called by God to denounce Ahab for this idolatry and to turn back to the worship of Jehovah. Elijah appeared before Ahab and said to him, "As the Lord God of Israel lives, before whom I stand, there shall not be dew or rain these years, except by my word."

Then the word of the Lord directed Elijah to turn eastward and hide himself by the brook Cherith, to the east of the Jordan. He was instructed to drink from the brook, and to eat the food which the ravens would bring him there. So he obeyed the word of the Lord and went and hid secretly by the brook Cherith. And for some time the ravens brought him bread and meat in the morning, and bread and meat in the evening; and he drank the clear water from the brook. But after a while the brook dried up, because there was no rain in the land.

Elijah was then directed to go to Zarephath, on the coast of the Mediterranean, north of Tyre, to live for a time. He was told that a poor widow would sustain him there. So he arose and traveled for many days until he came to Zarephath. When he came to the gate of the city, he saw a widow there gathering sticks to make a fire; and he called to her and said, "Bring me, I pray you, a little water in a vessel, so that I may drink." And as she was going to bring it he called to her and said, "Bring me, I pray you, a morsel of bread in your hand." The widow sadly replied, "As the Lord your God lives, I have not one cake, but only a handful of meal in a barrel and a little oil in a cruse; and behold, I am gathering some sticks so that I may go and cook it for myself and my son, so that we may eat it, and die."

Elijah spoke kindly to her and said, "Fear not; go and do as you have said; but first make me a little cake of it and bring it to me, and afterward make some for yourself and your son." Then he added, "For thus speaks the Lord God of Israel, 'The barrel of meal shall not be used up, and the cruse of oil shall not fail, until the day that the Lord sends rain upon the earth.'" The trusting widow went and did as Elijah said; and she, and the man

167

The ravens brought Elijah bread and meat

of God, and her family ate for many days. The barrel of meal was not used up, neither did the cruse of oil fail, according to the word of the Lord which he spoke through Elijah.

After this the son of the widow suddenly became sick and died. The bereaved mother said to Elijah, "What have you done to me, O you man of God? Have you come to me to recall my sin to memory and to slay my son?" Elijah quietly said to her, "Give me your son." And he took the child from her bosom, and carried him up into the upstairs room where he lodged, and laid him upon his own bed. Then the prophet prayed, "O Lord my God, have you also brought tragedy upon the widow with whom I sojourn by slaying her son?"

Then he stretched himself upon the child three times, and cried to the Lord, "O Lord my God, let this child's soul come into him again." The Lord heard Elijah's prayer, and the soul of the child came into him again and he revived. And Elijah took the child, and brought him down from the upstairs room into the house, and delivered him to his mother. And Elijah said to the astonished mother, "See, your son lives." And the happy mother said to Elijah, "Now I know that you are a man of God, and that the word of the Lord in your mouth is truth."

FIFTY-FOUR

Elijah's Contest With the Prophets of Baal

I Kings 18:1–46

IN the third year of the drought and famine, the Lord said to Elijah, "Go, show yourself to Ahab; and I will send rain upon the earth." So Elijah started to return to show himself to Ahab.

When the wicked king and the stern prophet finally came face to face, Ahab said to Elijah, "Is it you, the troubler of Israel?" Elijah answered, "I have not troubled Israel; but you have, and your father's house, in that you have forsaken the commandments of the Lord and have followed Baalim." Then the prophet of God commanded the king to send for and gather all Israel together at Mount Carmel, and the four hundred and fifty prophets of Baal and the four hundred prophets of the groves, who sat down at Jezebel's table.

So Ahab sent to all the children of Israel, and gathered the prophets together at Mount Carmel. Then Elijah addressed the people, saying, "How long are you going to hesitate between two opinions? If the Lord is God, follow him; but if Baal, then follow him." And the people did not answer him a word.

Then Elijah said to the people, "I, even I only, remain a prophet of the Lord; but Baal's prophets are four hundred and fifty men. Let them therefore give us two bullocks; and let them choose one bullock for themselves, and cut it in pieces and lay it on the wood, but put no fire under it; and I will get ready the other bullock and lay it on the wood, and put no fire under it. And you call on the name of your god and I will call on the name of the Lord; and the God who answers by fire, let him be God." And all the people answered, "It is well spoken."

Then Elijah said to the prophets of Baal, "You choose one bullock for yourselves and get it ready first, for you are many; and call on the name of your gods, but put no fire under it." They did as they were directed, and called on the name of Baal from morning until noon, saying, "O Baal, hear us." But there was neither voice nor did any answer.

And they staggered about the altar which they had made.

And at noon Elijah mocked them, saying, "Cry aloud, for he is a god; either he is talking, or he is pursuing, or he is on a journey, or perhaps he is asleep and must be awakened." And the prophets of Baal cried aloud, and cut themselves after their practice with knives and lances, until the blood gushed out upon them. And midday passed and still they ranted, until the time of the offering of the evening sacrifice; but there was neither voice, nor did any answer or any heed.

The fire of the Lord fell and consumed the burnt offering

Then Elijah said to all the people, "Come near me." And all the people came near him. And he repaired the altar of the Lord that had been pulled down. He took twelve stones, according to the number of the tribes of the sons of Jacob, and with the stones he built an altar in the name of the Lord.

He then made a shallow trench about the altar. And he put the wood in order, and cut the bullock in pieces and laid it on the wood. And he said, "Fill four barrels with water, and pour it on the burnt sacrifice and on the wood." He bade them do this a second time and a third time. And the water ran about the altar, and filled the trench also with water.

At the time of the offering of the evening sacrifice, Elijah the prophet came near and said, "Lord God of Abraham, Isaac, and Jacob, let it be known today that you are God in Israel and that I am your servant, and that I have done all these things at your word. Hear me, O Lord, hear me, so that this people may know that you are the Lord God, and that you have turned their hearts back again."

Then the fire of the Lord fell, and consumed the burnt offering, and also the wood, and the stones, and the dust, and licked up the water that was in the trench. And when all the people saw it, they fell on their faces and cried out, "The Lord, he is God; the Lord, he is God." And Elijah said to them, "Arrest all the prophets of Baal; let not one of them escape." And they were seized; and Elijah brought them down to the brook Kishon and there put them to death.

Afterward Elijah said to Ahab, "Get up, eat and drink; for there is a sound of an abundance of rain." So Ahab went up to eat and to drink. But Elijah went up to the top of Carmel; and he threw himself down upon the earth and put his face between his knees.

And Elijah said to his servant, "Go up now, look toward the sea." And he went up and looked, and said, "There is nothing." And Elijah said, "Go again seven times." And the seventh time the servant said, "Behold, there is coming up out of the sea a little cloud like a man's hand." Then Elijah said, "Go up, say to Ahab, 'Prepare your chariot and get down, so that the rain will not stop you.'"

In a little while the heavens grew black with clouds and wind, and there was a great rain. And Ahab rode in his chariot and went to Jezreel. And the hand of the Lord was on Elijah; and he girded up his loins and ran before Ahab to the entrance of Jezreel.

Elijah Hears a Still Small Voice

I Kings 19:1–21

BACK at the palace in Jezreel, Ahab told Jezebel all that Elijah had done, and how he had slain all the prophets of Baal with the sword. Jezebel's fury knew no bounds, and she sent a messenger to Elijah with this threatening message: "So let the gods do to me, and more also, if I do not make your life as the life of one of them by tomorrow about this time." Elijah was suddenly stricken with fear at this message, and he arose and fled for his life, and came to Beer-sheba, in the land of Judah, where he left his servant who had accompanied him.

Going on alone, Elijah went a day's journey into the wilderness, and came and sat down under a juniper tree. In a mood of black despair, the discouraged man requested that he might die, saying, "It is enough; now, O Lord, take away my life; for I am not any better than my fathers." And he lay down and went to sleep under the juniper tree.

And behold, an angel touched him and said, "Arise and eat." And Elijah woke up and looked, and behold, there was a cake baked on coals and a cruse of water at his head. And he ate and drank, and lay down again. And the angel of the Lord came to him a second time and said, "Arise and eat, otherwise the journey will be too great for you." So Elijah arose, and ate and drank, and went on the strength of that food for forty days and forty nights until he came to Horeb, the mount of God.

At Horeb Elijah found a cave and lodged there. And behold, the word of the Lord came to him, saying, "What are you doing here, Elijah?" Feeling sorry for himself, Elijah replied, "I have been very jealous for the Lord God of hosts; for the children of Israel have forsaken your covenant, thrown down your altars, and slain your prophets with the sword; and I, even I only, am left; and they seek my life, to take it away."

And the voice said, "Go forth, and stand upon the mount before the Lord." Elijah did so; and behold, the Lord passed by, and a great and strong wind split the mountains, and broke in pieces the rocks before the Lord, but the Lord was not in the wind. And after the wind there was an earthquake, but the Lord was not in the earthquake. And after the earthquake there was a fire, but the Lord was not in the fire. And after the fire there came a still small voice.

And when Elijah heard the still small voice, he wrapped his face in his mantle and went out and stood at the entrance of the cave. And behold, the voice said to him again, "What are you doing here, Elijah?" The prophet replied by repeating the words of his complaint. But the Lord healed Elijah's wounded spirit by telling him that he had further work to do.

And the Lord said to Elijah, "Go, return on your way to the wilderness of Damascus; and when you get there you shall anoint

When Elijah heard the still small voice he went out and stood at the entrance of the cave

Hazael to be king over Syria. And Jehu the son of Nimshi you shall anoint to be king over Israel. And Elisha the son of Shaphat of Abelmeholah you shall anoint to be prophet in your stead. And him who escapes the sword of Hazael shall Jehu slay; and him who escapes the sword of Jehu shall Elisha slay. Yet I have left seven thousand in Israel, all the knees that have not bowed to Baal, and every mouth that has not kissed him."

And so Elijah, armed with new courage and purpose, departed from Horeb in obedience to the word of the Lord. And he came and found Elisha the son of Shaphat, who was plowing, with twelve yoke of oxen before him,

and he was with the twelfth. Elijah passed by him and threw his mantle over him. And Elisha left the oxen, and ran after Elijah, and said, "Let me, I pray you, kiss my father and my mother, and then I will follow you."

And Elijah said to Elisha, "Go back again; for what have I done to you?" And Elisha turned back, and took a yoke of oxen, and killed them, and boiled their flesh by making a fire of the yokes of the oxen, and gave the meat to the people, and they ate of it. Elisha did these things to show the people that he was leaving his work as a farmer to become a prophet of the Lord. In due time he arose and went after Elijah, and ministered to him.

FIFTY-SIX

Elijah Denounces Ahab for Taking Naboth's Vineyard

I Kings 21:1–29

BESIDE King Ahab's summer palace and grounds in Jezreel, there was situated a splendid vineyard owned by a man by the name of Naboth. Ahab greatly desired to possess this vineyard in order to extend his already ample garden plots. So one day he said to Naboth in a very demanding tone, "Give me your vineyard, so that I may have it for an herb garden, because it is near my house; and I will give you a better vineyard for it; or, if it seems good to you,

I will give you what it is worth in money."

But Naboth did not want to part with his vineyard on any terms. His father and grandfather had lived there before him, and he felt duty-bound to keep the property within the family. So he gave this answer to Ahab, "The Lord forbids me to give you the inheritance of my fathers." This displeased Ahab very much, and he went into his house angry and displeased. Like a spoiled child, he lay down on his bed, turned his face to the wall, and would not eat anything that was brought to him.

But Jezebel his wife came into the room and asked the king, "Why is your spirit so sad that you will have nothing to eat?" Then Ahab told Jezebel how Naboth had refused to part with his vineyard. And then Queen Jezebel his wife answered, "Do you now govern the kingdom of Israel? Arise, and eat bread, and let your heart be merry; I will give you the vineyard of Naboth the Jezreelite."

Jezebel's plan to secure Naboth's vineyard was wicked and cruel. She wrote letters in Ahab's name to the elders and nobles of Jezreel and sealed them with the king's seal. In these letters she commanded the rulers to bring false charges against Naboth and have him stoned to death. The elders and nobles of the city did as Jezebel had commanded them. They took Naboth outside the city and stoned him to death with stones. Then they sent word to Jezebel, saying, "Naboth has been stoned, and is dead."

As soon as Jezebel received this message, she said to Ahab, "Arise, take possession of

Naboth's refusal to sell his vineyard greatly displeased King Ahab

the vineyard of Naboth the Jezreelite, which he refused to give you for money; for Naboth is no longer alive, but dead." When Ahab heard that Naboth was dead, he arose at once to go down to the vineyard of Naboth, to take possession of it.

At this juncture the word of the Lord came to Elijah the Tishbite, saying, "Arise, go down to meet Ahab king of Israel, who is in Samaria; behold, he is in the vineyard of Naboth, where he has gone to possess it." Furthermore, Elijah was instructed to say to Ahab, "Have you killed, and also taken possession? Thus says the Lord: 'In the place where dogs licked the blood of Naboth shall dogs lick your blood, even yours.'"

So it came to pass that while Ahab was walking in Naboth's vineyard, he was suddenly confronted with the prophet of the Lord. Ahab said to Elijah, "Have you found me, O my enemy?" Elijah answered, "I have found you, because you have sold yourself to do evil in the sight of the Lord." Then he warned Ahab concerning the punishment that would come upon him and his household for the wickedness that he and Jezebel had done.

Ahab was filled with fear and dismay as he heard the prophet's words. He was saddened to hear that not one of his children would go unpunished, and that Jezebel the queen would die a horrible death because she had influenced Ahab to do so much evil in the kingdom of Israel.

When Ahab heard the message of doom, he tore his clothes, dressed himself in sackcloth, and fasted, and went about sad and despondent. Then the Lord, seeing the penitence and grief of Ahab, said to the prophet Elijah, "Have you seen how Ahab has humbled himself before me? Because he has humbled himself before me I will not bring the evil in his days; but in his son's days I will bring the evil upon his house." That is to say, Ahab himself would die before the predicted punishments would be visited upon his wife Jezebel and their children.

Elijah Taken Up to Heaven

II Kings 2:1–18

THE time had come when Elijah's work as a prophet in Israel was completed, and when his earthly career was about to be ended. God had appointed Elisha to succeed Elijah and to carry on his work. Elijah knew that his remaining days on earth were few, and he wanted to visit the schools of the young prophets and say farewell to them before being taken away. So he and Elisha prepared to take their last journey together.

This memorable journey began at Gilgal, about seven miles northwest of Bethel. There Elijah said to his young companion, "Stay here, I pray you; for the Lord has sent me to Bethel." But Elisha replied, "As the Lord lives, and as your soul lives, I will not leave you." So they went down to Bethel together. And the sons of the prophets who were in Bethel came out to Elisha and said to him, "Do you not know that today the Lord will take away your master from you?" And Elisha answered, "Yes, I know it; hold your peace."

At Bethel, Elijah said to Elisha, "Stay here, I pray you; for the Lord has sent me to Jericho." But Elisha earnestly answered, "As the Lord lives, and as your soul lives, I will not leave you." So they arrived at Jericho. The sons of the prophets at Jericho drew near to Elisha and said to him, "Do you not know that today the Lord will take away your master from you?" And Elisha replied, "Yes, I know it; hold your peace."

As Elijah was about to leave Jericho, he said to Elisha, "Stay here, I pray you; for the Lord has sent me to the Jordan." But again Elisha declared, "As the Lord lives, and as your soul lives, I will not leave you." So the two of them went on together. Fifty men of the sons of the prophets also went after them, and stopped to watch from afar. Elijah and Elisha stood by the Jordan. And Elijah took his prophet's mantle, and wrapped it up, and struck the surface of the waters, and they were divided to each side so that the two of them could cross over on dry land.

When they had crossed over the Jordan, Elijah said to Elisha, "Ask what I shall do for you before I am taken away from you." And Elisha earnestly replied, "I pray you, let a double portion of your spirit be upon me." Elijah knew that only God could grant this request, so he said to Elisha, "You have asked a hard thing; nevertheless, if you see me when I am taken from you, it shall be so for you; but if not, it shall not be so."

And as they walked on, talking, behold, a chariot of fire and horses of fire suddenly appeared and came between them. And Elijah was taken up by a whirlwind into heaven. And Elisha saw this marvelous sight and cried out, "My father, my father, the chariots of Israel and their horsemen." Then the great whirlwind and the chariot and horses of fire and the form of the prophet Elijah disappeared from view, and Elisha saw him no more. Then Elisha took hold of his own clothes and tore

Elijah was taken up by a whirlwind into heaven

them in two pieces, as a sign of his own grief.

Elisha stooped and picked up the mantle of Elijah that had fallen to the ground, and went back and stood on the bank of the Jordan. Then he took the mantle of Elijah that had fallen from him, and struck the waters and said, "Where is the Lord God of Elijah?" And when he had struck the waters they divided to each side, and Elisha crossed over on dry ground.

Now when the sons of the prophets who had followed from Jericho saw Elisha by the Jordan, they said, "The spirit of Elijah rests on Elisha." And they came to meet him, and bowed to the ground before him, acknowledging him as their new master. And they said to him, "Behold now, there are with your servants fifty strong men; let them go, we pray you, and seek your master; it may be that the Spirit of the Lord has taken him up and flung him upon some mountain or into some valley." But Elisha, knowing that it was useless to search for the body of Elijah, commanded, "You shall not send."

But when they continued to urge him to let them search for Elijah, he relented and said, "Send." Therefore they sent fifty men; and for three days they searched the countryside for him. But of course they did not find Elijah, for he had been taken up to heaven. And the searchers came back to Elisha, who had stayed at Jericho, and reported that they had not found Elijah. And Elisha reminded them, "Did I not say to you, 'Go not'?" And Elisha remained for a time with the young men at the school of the prophets at Jericho.

FIFTY-EIGHT

Elisha Helps His Friends

II Kings 2:19–25; 4:1–7

SOON after Elijah was taken up to heaven, Elisha began his ministry of teaching the people, performing miracles, and helping the poor. By contrast with Elijah, the prophet of fire, Elisha may be called "the gentle prophet." Jehoram, son of Ahab, ruled as king of Israel from 853 to 842 B.C., and it was during his reign that Elisha served God and the children of Israel as a faithful prophet.

Elisha stayed for a while in Jericho with his friends, the sons of the prophets, after Elijah was taken from him. One day the men of the city said to Elisha, "Behold, we pray you, the situation of this city is pleasant, as my lord sees; but the water is polluted and the ground barren." The man of God replied, "Bring me a new cruse and put salt in it." And they brought it to him, wondering what he would do. Then Elisha went to the spring of water and threw salt in it, and said, "Thus says the Lord: 'I have healed these waters; there shall no longer be any death or barren land.'" So the water became pure, according

The widow poured oil into the vessels which her sons brought to her

to the word which Elisha the prophet spoke.

Then Elisha left Jericho and went to Bethel to visit the school of the prophets there. As the man of God drew near to Bethel, some children came out of the city and mocked him, saying, "Go up, you bald head! Go up, you bald head." Elisha turned to them and rebuked them in the name of the Lord. Thereupon two she-bears came out of the woods and tore forty-two of the children.

After Elisha's visit at Bethel, he went to Mount Carmel, where God had answered Elijah's prayer, and from there returned to Samaria, the capital of Israel.

When the kings of Israel, Judah, and Edom joined against Moab, they found no water for their armies in seven days' journey. The king of Judah sought advice from Elisha who told them to make ditches in the valley, and without their seeing rain or wind the valley would be filled. And it was as Elisha had said.

Now the wife of one of the sons of the prophets cried to Elisha, "Your servant my husband is dead; and you know that your servant feared the Lord, but now the creditor has come to take my two sons to be his servants." And Elisha asked the poor widow, "What shall I do for you? Tell me, what do you have in the house?" And she replied, "Your handmaiden has nothing in the house except a pot of oil."

Then Elisha instructed the widow, "Go forth, borrow vessels from all your neighbors —empty vessels and quite a few. Then go back into your house, shut the door upon yourself and your sons, and pour oil into all these vessels; and set them aside when they are full."

So the widow did as she was told, and went into her house and shut the door upon herself and her sons. And she began to pour the oil out of the pot which she had into the vessels which they brought to her. When all the vessels were full, she said to her son, "Bring me another vessel." And he said to her, "There are no more empty vessels." Then the oil flowed no longer. The widow came and told the man of God, and he said to her, "Go, sell the oil and pay your debt, and you and your children live on the rest."

Elisha Restores the Shunamite's Child

II Kings 4:8–37

Having helped the poor widow to save her sons, Elisha was in turn helped himself by a wealthy and generous woman of Shunem. One day he went to Shunem, a town situated some three miles northeast of Jezreel and about sixteen miles from Mount Carmel. A certain rich woman who lived there received him into her home and gave him food to eat. Elisha continued to stop there, whenever he passed by, and the good woman always fed him.

One day the woman said to her husband concerning Elisha, "Behold now, I perceive that this is a holy man of God who is continually passing by our house. Let us make a little room, and put there for him a bed, a table, a stool, and a candlestick, so that the next time he comes to us he will have a place to stay." Elisha greatly appreciated this kindness, and was glad to stay in their hospitable home whenever he came that way.

On a certain day Elisha came to his comfortable room and lay down there to rest. His servant Gehazi was with him, and he said to Gehazi, "Call the Shunamite woman." The good woman came and stood before Gehazi. Elisha directed Gehazi to say to her, "Behold, you have shown us all this kindness; what is to be done for you? Would you have a word spoken on your behalf to the king, or to the commander of the army?" But she humbly answered, "I live among my own people." By this she meant that she was not asking any special favor for herself in return for her kindness to Elisha and his servant Gehazi.

Elisha then said to Gehazi, "What then is to be done for her?" Gehazi replied, "She has no child and her husband is old." Elisha said, "Call her." Presently the Shunamite woman stood in the doorway, and Elisha said to her, "About this season, when a year has gone by, you shall embrace a son." The woman, greatly amazed, responded, "Oh no, my lord, you man of God; do not lie to your handmaiden." But as the prophet had said to her, the woman conceived and gave birth to a son at that season a year later.

A number of years passed, and when the child was grown he went out one day among the reapers in the field to his father. Suddenly the child became ill, and cried out to his father, "My head, my head." The father quickly said to one of his men, "Carry him to his mother." The servant lifted the sick child in his arms and carried him into the house to his mother. The little boy sat on his mother's knees until noon, and then he died.

The grief-stricken mother went up and laid him on the bed of the man of God, and shut the door on him and went out. She then called to her husband and said, "Send me, I pray you, one of your men, and one of the asses, so that I may hasten to the man of God and come back again." The husband said, "Why will you go to him today? It is neither new moon nor sabbath." She replied, "It shall be well." Then she saddled an ass and said to her servant, "Drive quickly and do not

The Shunamite woman fell at Elisha's feet in gratitude

slacken the pace for me until I say to." So she departed on her urgent journey, and presently came to Elisha at Mount Carmel.

When the man of God saw her coming, he said to Gehazi his servant, "Behold, here comes the Shunamite woman; run now, I pray you, to meet her, and say to her, 'Is it well with you? Is it well with your husband? Is it well with the child?'" The good woman answered Gehazi, "It is well." And when she came to Elisha, she caught hold of his feet. Gehazi came near to thrust her away, but Elisha said, "Let her alone, for she is sorely distressed; and the Lord has hidden it from me, and has not told me." Then the grieving mother said, "Did I ask my lord to give me a son? Did I not say, 'Do not deceive me'?"

Elisha then said to Gehazi, "Gird your loins, take my staff in your hand, and go your way. If you meet any man, do not greet him, and if any man greets you, do not answer him; and lay my staff upon the face of the child." And the mother of the child said, "As the Lord lives, and as your soul lives, I will not leave you." So Elisha arose and followed her toward Shunem. Gehazi went ahead of

them and laid Elisha's staff upon the face of the child, but he heard no sound from it and saw no sign of life. Whereupon Gehazi went back to meet Elisha, and told him, "The child has not awakened."

When Elisha came into the house, he saw the child lying dead on his bed. He went in and shut the door, and prayed to the Lord. And then he went up and lay upon the child, and put his mouth upon his mouth, his eyes upon his eyes, and his hands upon his hands; and as he stretched himself upon him, the flesh of the child grew warm. Then he arose, walked to and fro in the house, and then went up and stretched himself upon the child again. Whereupon the child sneezed seven times and opened his eyes.

Then Elisha sent for Gehazi and said, "Call this Shunamite." So Gehazi called the child's mother. And when she came to Elisha, he spoke to her tenderly and said, "Take up your son." The mother came into the room, fell at the feet of the man of God, and bowed herself to the ground. Then in an ecstasy of joy, she took her son into her arms and went out to tell the child's father.

Elisha Heals Naaman's Leprosy

II Kings 5:1–27

ONE of the most notable miracles performed by Elisha, in the name and power of the God of Israel, was the healing of Naaman the leper. Naaman was a distinguished soldier, commander of the army of Ben-hadad, the king of Syria, whose capital was at Damascus. He was a great man in many ways, and was held in high favor by the king, because by his hand the Lord had granted victory to Syria. Naaman was a mighty man of valor, but he was a leper.

Some time before this, a band of Syrians had gone out on a raid and had taken captive a little maid from the land of Israel, along with the other things which they stole from the Israelites. This little girl became a maid-servant of Naaman's wife. She said to Naaman's wife, "Would that my master were with the prophet who is in Samaria! He would heal him of his leprosy." When Naaman heard this, he went and told King Ben-hadad what the little Hebrew maid had said. And the king of Syria said to Naaman, "Go on, and I will send a letter to the king of Israel on your behalf."

So Naaman, filled with new hope, set forth on his mission, taking with him as a present to King Jehoram ten talents of silver, six thousand pieces of gold, and ten changes of raiment. And he presented to the king of Israel Ben-hadad's letter, which said, "When this letter comes to you, know that I have sent you Naaman my servant, so that you may heal him of his leprosy."

But King Jehoram misunderstood the purpose of King Ben-hadad's request, and thought that the king of Syria was seeking an excuse to make war against Israel. Thus, when the king of Israel read the letter, he tore his clothes and said, "Am I God, with power to kill and to make alive, that this man sends to me to heal a man of his leprosy? Wherefore consider, I pray you, and you will see how he is seeking to quarrel with me."

But when Elisha the man of God heard how King Jehoram had reacted to the letter, he sent this message to the king of Israel: "Why have you torn your clothes? Let him come to me now and he shall know that there is a prophet in Israel."

So Naaman came with his prancing horses and splendid chariot, and stopped at the door of Elisha's humble abode. In order to humble this proud warrior, and let him know that it was by the power of the God of Israel that he was to be healed, Elisha did not go out in person to see Naaman. Instead he sent a messenger to him, saying, "Go and wash in the Jordan seven times, and your flesh shall be restored to you, and you shall be clean."

But this made the proud and haughty soldier very angry, and he at first gave no heed to Elisha's instructions. He stubbornly said to his companions, "Behold, I thought, 'He will surely come out to me, and stand, and call on the name of the Lord his God, and move his hand over the place, and heal the leprosy.'" In the same vein of foolish pride, Naaman continued, "Are not Abana and

Naaman dipped himself in the river Jordan

Pharpar, rivers of Damascus, better than all the waters of Israel? May I not wash in them and be clean?" So he turned and went away in a rage.

But Naaman's servants, who were wiser than he, came up to him and said, "My father, if the prophet had bidden you to do some great thing, would you not have done it? How much rather, then, should you do this simple thing that he asked you to do, when he said, 'Wash, and be clean'?" Naaman heeded this good advice and went down and dipped himself seven times in the river Jordan, according to the word of the prophet Elisha; and his flesh became again like the flesh of a little child, and he was healed of his leprosy.

Then Naaman returned to the man of God, he and all his company, and he came and stood before Elisha and said, "Behold, now I know that there is no God in all the earth but in Israel; now therefore accept a gift from your servant." But Elisha declined, saying, "As the Lord lives, before whom I stand, I will not accept a gift for this work of God." Naaman urged him to take the present, but Elisha steadfastly refused.

Then, to show his gratitude and sincerity, Naaman proposed another plan. He asked Elisha for permission to take two mules' burden of earth from the land of Israel back to Damascus. He promised that he would build an altar upon this sacred ground, and that he would offer sacrifices and offerings only to the God of Israel.

Naaman also asked the Lord to pardon him for the things he would have to do in performing his duties to the king of Syria. It was customary for the king of Syria to lean on Naaman's arm when he went to the house of Rimmon to worship this false god. It would be necessary for Naaman to bow down with his king in the house of Rimmon, and he desired that the Lord pardon him for this apparent act of worship in the performance of his civil duty. Elisha commended Naaman for his honest purpose, and said to the leper who had been made whole, "Go in peace."

When Naaman had traveled a short distance, Elisha's servant Gehazi ran after him to get for himself part of the gift Elisha had refused to accept from Naaman for the work of the Lord. Gehazi pretended he had been sent to get a present for two visiting sons of the prophets, and Naaman graciously gave him more than he asked for. When Gehazi returned home, Elisha asked him where he had been. The servant did not tell the truth, and Elisha, who knew of the wrongdoing, punished him by causing him and his descendants to become lepers as Naaman once had been.

Elisha and the Chariots of Fire

II Kings 6:1–23

ONCE when Elisha was visiting the sons of the prophets in a certain place, the young men said to him, "Behold now, the place where we live with you is too crowded for us. Let us go, we pray you, to the Jordan. If each of us takes a log from there we can make a place there to live." Elisha answered, "Go ahead." Then one of them said, "Please be glad and go with your servants." And Elisha replied, "I will go." So he went with them.

And when they came to the Jordan they cut down trees. And it came to pass that as one of them was felling a tree, his axe head fell into the deep water. The young man was greatly disturbed by this, because he thought he would not be able to recover the axe head. So he called to Elisha and said, "Alas, my master, the axe head was borrowed."

Then the man of God asked, "Where did it fall into the water?" When the young man showed Elisha the place, he cut down a stick and threw it into the water, causing the iron axe head to float up to the surface. And he said to the young man, "Take it up again." And he stretched out his hand and took it.

Soon after this incident Ben-hadad the king of Syria made war against Israel. He took counsel with his servants, saying, "At such and such a place our army will camp." But this was made known to Elisha the prophet, and he sent word to the king of Israel, "Beware that you do not pass this place, for the Syrians are going down there." So King Jehoram sent his soldiers to defend the place of which the man of God had told him. Elisha gave warnings to the king of Israel so that he was prepared ahead of time to ward off the Syrian attacks on several occasions.

The king of Syria was greatly troubled over the failure of his plans to launch his surprise attacks. He thought some of his own soldiers were betraying his plans to the Israelites. So he called his servants and said to them, "Will you not find out who is helping the king of Israel?" And one of his servants replied, "None, my lord, O king; but Elisha, the prophet who is in Israel, tells the king of Israel the words that you speak in your bedroom." Whereupon the king commanded, "Go and find out where he is, so that I may send to get him." It was told the king, "Behold, the prophet is in Dothan." So he sent there horses and chariots and a great army; and they came by night and encircled the city.

When Elisha's servant rose early the next morning and went out, behold, an army with horses and chariots surrounded the city. In great fear the servant ran to Elisha and said, "Alas, my master, what shall we do?" The prophet of God calmly said, "Fear not, for those that are with us are more than those that are with them."

And Elisha prayed, and said, "Lord, I pray you, open his eyes so that he may see." So the

Lord opened the eyes of the young man and he saw; and behold, the mountain was full of horses and chariots of fire round about Elisha.

When the Syrians came down to attack the city, Elisha prayed to the Lord, saying, "Strike this people down, I pray you, with blindness." God answered his prayer, and all of the Syrian soldiers were stricken with blindness. Elisha then said to the blind company, "This is not the way, nor is this the city; follow me and I will bring you to the man you are looking for." But he led them to the city of Samaria.

Upon entering Samaria, Elisha prayed, "Lord, open the eyes of these men so that they may see." So the Lord opened their eyes and they saw; and behold, they were in the middle of Samaria. And when the king of Israel saw all these enemy prisoners within his city, he said to Elisha, "My father, shall I kill them? Shall I put them to death?"

But the prophet of the Lord replied, "You shall not kill them. Would you kill those whom you had taken captive with your sword or with your bow? Set bread and water before them, and let them eat and drink and then go to their master." So the king of Israel pre-

The mountain was full of horses and chariots of fire

pared a great feast for these enemy soldiers; and when they had eaten and drunk, he sent them away, and they went to their master.

This act of mercy and kindness on the part of the king of Israel made a great impression upon the king of Syria and his people. And the Syrians made no more raids into the land of Israel.

SIXTY-TWO

The Prophet Jonah Preaches at Nineveh

Jonah 1:1–4:11

JONAH was a prophet of Israel during the reign of King Jeroboam II. He was born in a village of Galilee, Gath-hepher by name, and his father was Amittai. His special mission in life was to proclaim the word of the Lord to the people of Nineveh, the great capital city of the kingdom of Assyria.

The word of the Lord came to Jonah, saying, "Arise, go to Nineveh, that great city, and cry against it; for their wickedness has come up before me." But Jonah at first disobeyed the word of the Lord and sought to flee from His presence. He went down to the harbor of Joppa and found a ship going to Tarshish. So Jonah paid the fare and went aboard the ship to go with the mariners to Tarshish away from the Lord's presence.

But the Lord sent a great wind and a mighty tempest upon the sea, so that the ship was in danger of breaking up. The mariners were afraid of perishing, and each cried to his god; and they tossed the ship's cargo into the sea to lighten it. But Jonah had gone down into the hold of the ship and lain down, and was fast asleep. So the ship's captain came to him and said, "What do you mean by sleep-

ing? Arise, call upon your God, so that He might give us some thought and keep us from perishing."

The mariners said to one another, "Come, let us cast lots, so that we can find out who is to blame for this evil which has come upon us." They cast lots, and the lot fell upon Jonah. Then they said to him, "Tell us, we pray you, are you to blame for this evil which has come upon us? What is your occupation? And where do you come from? What is your country? And of what people are you?"

Jonah answered, "I am a Hebrew; and I fear the Lord, the God of heaven, who has made the sea and the dry land." Then the mariners were exceedingly afraid, and said to him, "Why have you done this?" For the seamen knew that he was fleeing from the presence of the Lord, because he had told them.

Then the sailors asked Jonah, "What shall we do to you to make the sea calm again?" for the sea lashed the ship and was tempestuous. Jonah submissively replied, "Take me up and throw me overboard into the sea; so shall the sea be calmed again; for I know that this great tempest has come upon you on account of me." Nevertheless the sailors rowed hard to

The sailors took up Jonah and threw him overboard into the sea

bring the ship back to land, but they could not, for the sea lashed harder and was even more tempestuous.

When their efforts availed nothing, the mariners cried to the Lord, "We beseech you, O Lord, we beseech you, do not let us perish for this man's life, and do not lay upon us innocent blood; for you, O Lord, have done as you pleased." So they took up Jonah and threw him overboard into the sea; and the sea stopped raging. Then the seamen feared the Lord exceedingly, and they offered a sacrifice to the Lord and made vows.

And the Lord designated a great fish to swallow up Jonah; and Jonah was in the belly of the fish three days and three nights. In his distress Jonah prayed earnestly to the Lord his God from the belly of the fish asking God mercifully to deliver him. And the Lord heard the prayer of Jonah, and the Lord spoke to the fish, and it vomited out Jonah upon the dry land.

Then the word of the Lord came to Jonah the second time, saying, "Arise, go to Nineveh, that great city, and preach to it the message that I bid you." So Jonah arose and went to Nineveh, according to the word of the Lord.

Now Nineveh was such a large city that it was a three-day journey to pass through it. Jonah entered the city, going a day's journey. And as he went he cried, "Yet forty days and Nineveh shall be overthrown!" So the people of Nineveh believed God. As a sign of their penitence, they proclaimed a fast, and put on sackcloth, from the greatest of them to the least of them.

When the tidings of what was done reached the king of Nineveh, he arose from his throne, took off his royal robe, and covered himself with sackcloth and sat in ashes. Then he made a proclamation which was published through Nineveh by royal decree: "Let neither man nor beast, herd nor flock, taste anything; let them not feed, nor drink water, but let man and beast be covered with sackcloth, and cry mightily to God; indeed, let everyone turn from his evil way and from the violence that is in his hands. Who can tell but that God may yet repent and turn from his fierce anger, so that we will not perish?"

And God saw what the king and the people did, and how they turned from their evil way; and God regretted the evil which he had said he would do to them, and he did not do it.

This should have pleased the prophet of the Lord. But instead it displeased Jonah exceedingly, and he was very angry. And Jonah prayed to the Lord and said, "I pray you, O Lord, were these not my words when I was still in my own country? Therefore I fled to Tarshish; for I knew that you are a gracious God, and merciful, slow to anger, and of great kindness, and were sorry for the evil. Therefore now, O Lord, take my life from me, for it is better for me to die than to live."

And the Lord said to his aggrieved servant, "Is it well for you to be angry?" Then Jonah went out of Nineveh and sat down to the east of the city, making a booth for himself there. He sat under it in the shade, till he might see what would become of the city.

And the Lord God caused a plant to come up over Jonah to provide shade for his head and to spare him discomfort. So Jonah was exceedingly glad for the plant and the shade it provided. But when dawn came the next day, God caused a worm to attack the plant, so that it withered.

When the sun rose, God sent down a sultry east wind, and the sun beat upon the head of Jonah until he felt faint and wished that he might die, and said, "It is better for me to die than to live." Then God said to Jonah, "Is it well for you to be angry about the plant?" And Jonah sullenly replied, "I do well to be angry, even to death."

Then the Lord said to Jonah, "You have had pity on the plant, for which you did not labor or make grow; which came up in a night and perished in a night. And should I not spare Nineveh, that great city, where there are more than a hundred and twenty thousand persons who cannot discern between their right hand and their left hand; and also much cattle?"

VI.

STORIES

ABOUT THE

JEWS IN

CAPTIVITY

Daniel's Purpose Not To Defile Himself

Daniel 1:1–21

DANIEL was a great Jewish prophet who served the God of Israel in Babylon at the court of King Nebuchadnezzar. By birth he was the son of a royal family of the tribe of Judah; but as a youth he was carried away into captivity, along with many other Jews, by the king of Babylon, after his first siege of Jerusalem in 605 B.C. This was during the third year of the reign of Jehoiakim, king of Judah.

At the court of Babylon, Daniel was selected with other young captives of noble birth to be trained for state service. The king commanded the master of his eunuchs, Ashpenaz, to choose some of the Israelite youths of royal lineage and of the aristocracy for this special training. They were to be physically strong, good-looking, intelligent, wise, quick to learn, and capable of serving in the king's palace. They were to be taught the language and learning of the Chaldeans.

The king assigned them a special table where they were to eat the rich food which the king ate, and to drink the wine which he drank. They would receive training for three years, and at the end of that time would be ready to serve the king. Among these were four splendid youths of the tribe of Judah whose Hebrew names were Daniel, Hananiah, Mishael, and Azariah. The Chaldean names given them by the master of the eunuchs were Belteshazzar, Shadrach, Meshach, and Abednego.

But Daniel determined not to defile himself by eating the king's food, or drinking his wine. According to his religious training, these things were forbidden. So he asked the master of the eunuchs for permission not to defile himself. The Lord gave Daniel favor in the sight of the officer, so that he was willing to consider Daniel's request. But he pointed out to Daniel that the king, who appointed their food and drink, might see that they were not thriving as well as the others. Then, the eunuch said, he would be in danger of being put to death.

But Daniel suggested to the steward who prepared their food and drink that they be permitted to try this plan: "Put your servants to the test," said Daniel, "for a period of ten days; let us be given beans to eat and water to drink. Then compare our appearance with that of the youths who eat of the king's food, and decide how you will deal with your servants."

The steward agreed to try this proposal, and so he tested them for ten days. At the end of ten days it was clearly seen that they looked healthier and fatter than all the youths who ate of the king's food. After that the steward took away their portion of the king's food and the wine they were to drink, and gave them beans.

The God of their fathers was favorable to these four youths, and gave them knowledge and skill in all learning and wisdom. And Daniel had the special gift of understanding in all visions and dreams.

At the end of the three years of training, when the king had instructed that they be brought before him, the master of the eunuchs brought them in before Nebuchadnezzar. And the king conferred with them, and among them all none was found like Daniel, Hananiah, Mishael, and Azariah. Therefore they were chosen as worthy of serving the king.

The king examined the Hebrew youths by asking them all kinds of difficult questions, and in all matters of wisdom and understanding of which he inquired of them he found them ten times better than all the magicians and astrologers in his whole realm. So these earnest and faithful young noblemen served the king and their own people for many years to come.

Daniel determined not to defile himself by eating the king's food or drinking his wine

Daniel Interprets Nebuchadnezzar's Dream

Daniel 2:1–49

Not long after Daniel and his three friends were numbered among the wise men in Babylon, King Nebuchadnezzar had a dream that troubled him greatly. He believed his dream must have some important meaning, and he decided to ask his wise men to interpret it for him. So the king commanded that all the magicians and wise men of the kingdom be summoned to the palace to interpret his dream. And in due time they came and stood before the king.

Nebuchadnezzar said to the wise men, "I have had a dream, and my spirit is troubled to know the meaning of the dream." The Chaldeans replied, "O king, live forever; tell your servants the dream and we will give the interpretation." But the king could not remember his dream, and demanded that the wise men tell him both the dream and its meaning! If they could not do this, they would be put to death; but if they could make known the dream and its interpretation, they would receive gifts and honors from the king.

The Chaldeans thought the king's request was unreasonable, and said to him, "There is not a man upon the earth who can reveal this matter to the king; there is no king, lord, or ruler who has ever asked such a thing of any magician or astrologer or Chaldean. It is a rare thing that the king asks, and there is no one who can do it for the king except the gods, whose dwelling is not with flesh."

This made the king furiously angry, and he commanded that all the wise men of Babylon be destroyed. So the king's decree went forth that the wise men were to be slain, and they sought Daniel and the other youths, to slay them also. Then Daniel spoke with consideration and wisdom to Arioch, the captain of the king's guard, who had been sent to slay the wise men of Babylon. Daniel asked the king's captain, "Why is the decree of the king so hasty?" Then Arioch explained the matter to Daniel. And Daniel went in and besought the king to set a time for him to interpret the king's dream.

Then Daniel went to his own house and told his three companions what had happened. So the four young men prayed earnestly to the God of heaven to reveal the mystery to Daniel, so that they might not perish with the rest of the wise men of Babylon. That very night God showed Daniel in a vision the substance and meaning of Nebuchadnezzar's dream.

Daniel blessed the God of heaven who had wisdom and might, and revealed the deep and secret things, and he offered a prayer of praise and thanksgiving to God for the wisdom and strength He had given him. Then he hurried to Arioch, the king's captain, and said to him, "Do not destroy the wise men of Babylon; bring me in before the king and I will give him the interpretation of his dream."

Arioch was glad, and he quickly brought Daniel before the king, and said, "I have found among the captives from Judah a man who will make known the king's dream and its meaning." The king asked Daniel, "Can you make known to me the dream that I have seen and its interpretation?" Then Daniel explained to the king that the power to interpret his dream had been given to him by the God of heaven, and that no wise man on earth could know such secrets and reveal them.

Then Daniel revealed to Nebuchadnezzar the substance of his strange dream. "You saw in your dream, O king, a great image of extreme brightness standing before you, and its aspect was terrifying. The head of this image was of fine gold, its breast and arms of silver, its waist and thighs of brass, its legs of iron, its feet partly of iron and partly of clay. As you watched, a stone was cut out by unseen hands, and it struck the image on its feet of iron and clay and broke them in pieces. Then the iron, the clay, the brass, the silver, and the gold were all broken in pieces together, and became like the chaff of the summer threshing floors; and the wind carried them away, so that not a vestige of them was found. And the stone that broke the image became a great mountain, and filled the whole earth."

As the perplexed king listened eagerly to the young prophet's words, Daniel continued, "This is the dream; we will now give the king its interpretation: This great image represents four great earthly kingdoms. The kingdom of Babylon is the first, and the head of gold represents your great kingdom. After you shall arise another kingdom not as great as yours,

represented by the breast and arms of silver. Then there will be a third kingdom, represented by the waist and thighs of brass, which will rule over all the earth. And there shall be a fourth kingdom, shown by its legs of iron and its feet of iron and clay. This fourth kingdom will be very strong for a time; but afterward it will become divided, grow weak, and fall, because the iron in the feet is mixed with clay.

"And in the days of those kings," Daniel explained, "the God of heaven will set up a kingdom which shall never be destroyed, and this divine kingdom is represented by the great stone cut out of the mountain by unseen hands. This kingdom of God will increase until it fills the whole earth, and it will endure after all other kingdoms have perished." Then Daniel concluded, "The great God has made known to the king what shall come to pass hereafter. The dream is certain, and the interpretation sure."

King Nebuchadnezzar was amazed at the wisdom of the young Hebrew prophet, and he bowed with respect before Daniel, and commanded that an oblation and incense be offered up to him. The king said to Daniel, "Surely your God is a God of gods and a Lord of kings, and a revealer of secrets, since you were able to reveal this secret." Then Nebuchadnezzar bestowed high honors and many great gifts upon Daniel, and made him ruler over the whole province of Babylon, and chief governor over all the wise men of Babylon.

At Daniel's request, the king appointed his three companions, who were known to the king as Shadrach, Meshach, and Abednego, to positions of high honor and reward, and they governed the affairs of the province of Babylon. But Daniel remained as a valued and trusted counselor at the king's court.

Daniel revealed to Nebuchadnezzar the substance of his strange dream

The men were walking in the middle of the fire

Daniel's Friends Are Thrown Into the Fiery Furnace

Daniel 3:1–30

THE kingdom of Nebuchadnezzar, which in the king's dream was represented by the head of gold, grew in greatness and power, as many lands and peoples were added to his domain. The king became very proud and haughty and thought of himself as a very great person indeed.

Then Nebuchadnezzar decided to make a god and compel all the peoples of his kingdom to worship that god. He made a great image of gold that was nine feet wide and ninety feet high. He caused this golden image to be set up in the plain of Dura, in the province of Babylon.

The king then issued a command to assemble the princes, the governors, the captains, the judges, the treasurers, the counselors, the sheriffs, and all the rulers of the provinces to come to the dedication of the golden image which he had set up. Accordingly a vast company of these notable officials from many lands came together in the plain of Dura before the golden image.

A herald of the king then announced to the assembled throng, "You are commanded, O peoples, nations, and languages, when you hear the sound of the cornet, flute, harp, sackbut, psaltery, dulcimer, and every kind of music, to fall down and worship the golden image that King Nebuchadnezzar has set up; and whoever does not fall down and worship shall instantly be thrown into the middle of a burning fiery furnace."

Therefore when all the peoples heard the sound of the music, they bowed down and worshiped the golden image. But Daniel's three friends Shadrach, Meshach, and Abednego refused to bow down and worship this false god. Then certain of the Chaldeans, who were jealous of Daniel and his friends, reported their disobedience to King Nebuchadnezzar. They reminded the king of the decree he had issued requiring all peoples to bow down and worship the golden image, and of the punishment he had decreed for those who disobeyed. Then they said, "There are certain Jews whom you have appointed to rule over the affairs of the province of Babylon: Shadrach, Meshach, and Abednego. These men, O king, pay no attention to you; they do not serve your gods or worship the golden image which you have set up."

Then Nebuchadnezzar in rage and fury commanded that these disobedient Jews be brought before him. So the noble young Hebrews were brought before the king. Nebuchadnezzar said to them, "Is it true, O Shadrach, Meshach, and Abednego, that you do not serve my gods or worship the golden image which I have set up?" Then he offered them another chance to obey.

But the courageous young men, who worshiped only the God of Israel, answered the king, "O Nebuchadnezzar, it is not necessary for us to answer you in this matter. If it be so, our God whom we serve is able to deliver us safely from the burning fiery furnace; and He will deliver us out of your hand, O king. But if not, be it known to you, O king, that we will not serve your gods or worship the golden image which you have set up."

But Nebuchadnezzar did not appreciate their brave and noble answer. He was filled with fury at their stubborn refusal and was determined to make them suffer for their disobedience. He ordered the furnace heated seven times hotter than it was usually heated. And he commanded some of his mightiest warriors to bind Shadrach, Meshach, and Abednego with stout ropes, and to throw them into the burning fiery furnace.

Then these three young men were bound, fully clothed, and thrown, like chunks of wood, into the middle of the roaring furnace. And because the furnace was so very hot, the flame of the fire leaped out and killed the soldiers who threw them into the furnace. But Shadrach, Meshach, and Abednego fell bound into the middle of the burning fiery furnace.

Then King Nebuchadnezzar, who was watching from his royal chair, rose up in astonishment and great haste. Looking into the furnace from a safe distance, he said to his counselors, "Did we not throw three men bound into the middle of the fire?" They replied, "True, O king." The king answered, "Lo, I see four men loose, walking in the middle of the fire, and they are not hurt; and the aspect of the fourth is like the Son of God."

Then Nebuchadnezzar drew near to the entrance of the burning fiery furnace and said, "Shadrach, Meshach, and Abednego, you servants of the most high God, come forth, come here." Then the three young men came out of the fire. And the counselors of the king gathered around and saw that the fire had not hurt the bodies of the young men; not a hair of their heads was singed, their garments had not been affected, and no smell of fire had enveloped them.

The astonished king said, "Blessed be the God of Shadrach, Meshach, and Abednego, who has sent his angel and delivered his servants who trusted in him, and disregarded the king's command, and yielded up their bodies rather than serve and worship any god except their own God. Therefore I make a decree: That every people, nation, and language which speaks anything amiss against the God of Shadrach, Meshach, and Abednego shall be cut in pieces, and their houses razed to the ground; because there is no other god who is able to deliver in this fashion."

Then the king promoted Shadrach, Meshach, and Abednego to places of higher trust and honor in the kingdom of Babylon.

Daniel Interprets the Handwriting on the Wall

Daniel 5:1–31

AFTER a long reign of forty-three years, King Nebuchadnezzar died in the year 562 B.C. About twenty years after his death, a new king came to the throne whose name was Belshazzar. He was a wicked king, and his reign was of short duration.

During the third year of his reign, King Belshazzar made a great feast in his splendid palace at Babylon. He invited a thousand princes and nobles to share this feast with him and his many wives. It was a night of feasting, much drinking of wine, and revelry in Belshazzar's palace.

Belshazzar, when he had drunk too much wine, commanded that the vessels of gold and of silver which Nebuchadnezzar his father had taken out of the temple in Jerusalem be brought, so that the king and his princes, his wives, and his concubines might drink from them. When this was done, they proceeded to drink wine from these sacred vessels and to praise the gods of gold and silver, brass, iron, wood, and stone. Swift punishment came upon them for this act of sacrilege.

Almost instantly the fingers of a man's hand appeared and wrote opposite the candle holder on the plaster of the wall of the king's palace, and the king saw the part of the hand that wrote. Then the king turned pale, and his thoughts were troubled; his legs no longer supported him, and his knees trembled violently. Then he cried aloud for the astrologers, the Chaldeans, and the soothsayers.

Filled with apprehension, the king said to his wise men, "Whoever can read this writing, and give me its interpretation, shall be clothed with scarlet, and have a chain of gold about his neck, and shall be the third ruler in the kingdom." But when the wise men looked at the writing they could not read it or reveal to the king its interpretation. This made Belshazzar even more fearful, and his lords were greatly dismayed.

Then the queen, hearing about the commotion, came into the banqueting hall and sought to calm the fears of the king. She said to Belshazzar: "There is a man in your kingdom, in whom is the spirit of the holy gods. In the days of your father this man had wisdom and understanding like that of the gods; for which reason King Nebuchadnezzar made him master of all the wise men of Babylon. This man, Daniel, whom the king named Belteshazzar, had the power to interpret dreams and solve riddles and conflicts. Now therefore let Daniel be called, and he will give the interpretation."

Then Daniel was brought in before the king. Belshazzar commended Daniel for all the good things he had heard about him. He explained the matter that troubled him, and

Daniel read the writing on the wall and gave its interpretation

pointed out how his wise men were unable to interpret the strange writing on the wall. He promised to give Daniel a rich reward if he would read the writing and give its interpretation.

Then Daniel answered the troubled king, saying, "Let your gifts be for yourself, and give your rewards to another; yet I will read the writing to the king and make known its meaning." Speaking as a prophet of the Lord, Daniel then told the king why all these things had come to pass.

"O king," Daniel said, "the most high God gave Nebuchadnezzar your father a kingdom and majesty and glory and honor. And on account of the majesty that he gave him, all peoples, nations, and languages trembled and feared before him: whomever he would he put to death, and whomever he would he kept alive; whomever he would he set up, and whomever he would he put down.

"But when his heart was lifted up and his mind hardened in pride, he was deposed from his kingly throne and they took his glory from him. He was driven from the sons of men, and his heart was made like that of the beasts, and his dwelling was with the wild asses. They fed him grass like an ox, and his body was wet with the dew of heaven, until he knew that God rules in the kingdom of men and that he appoints over it whomever he will.

"And you his son, O Belshazzar, have not humbled your heart, though you knew all this, but have exalted yourself against the Lord of heaven. The vessels of God's house have been brought in before you, and you, your lords, your wives, and your concubines have drunk wine from them. You have praised the gods of silver and gold, of brass, iron, wood, and stone, which do not see or hear or know; and the God in whose hand is your breath, and to whom belongs all your ways, you have not glorified.

"Thus from God's presence the hand was sent, and this writing was inscribed. And this is the writing that was inscribed: MENE, MENE, TEKEL, UPHARSIN. This is the interpretation of the writing: MENE—God has numbered the years of your kingdom and made an end of it; TEKEL—you have been weighed in the balance and found wanting; PERES—your kingdom is divided and given to the Medes and Persians."

Then Belshazzar gave the command and they clothed Daniel with scarlet, and put a chain of gold about his neck, and made a proclamation concerning him, that he should be the third ruler in the kingdom.

But Belshazzar's attempt to appease the prophet of the Lord could not change the divine verdict. His doom was sealed. That very night Belshazzar the Chaldean king was slain. The Persian armies captured the city of Babylon, and King Darius took over the kingdom of the Chaldeans.

Daniel Is Delivered From the Lions' Den

Daniel 6:1–28

KING Darius, the new ruler of Babylon, was sixty-two years old when he received the kingdom. He chose a hundred and twenty princes to govern the many provinces of his vast kingdom. Over these princes he appointed three presidents, to whom the princes should render account, so that the king's affairs might be properly managed. Daniel was one of these three presidents, and because he was the most eminent of all the princes and presidents for his wisdom and counsel, he was made the chief president over the whole kingdom.

The other presidents and princes became very jealous and envious of Daniel because the king had honored him above themselves. So they sought some occasion to complain about Daniel so that they might discredit him in the eyes of King Darius. But they could find no occasion or fault of which to complain, inasmuch as Daniel was faithful in every respect and was guilty of no error or fault. Then these evil men said among themselves, "We shall not find any occasion to complain against this Daniel except perhaps concerning the law of his God."

So they watched Daniel carefully and observed that it was his custom to kneel down before his window every day and pray to the God of Israel. This gave them the idea for a wicked and cruel plot by which they might entrap Daniel.

The company of princes and presidents, all except Daniel, came before the king and said, "King Darius, live forever. All the presidents of the kingdom and all the princes are agreed that the king should establish a statute and make a firm decree that whoever presents a petition to any god or man for thirty days, except to you O king, shall be thrown into the den of lions. Now, O king, establish the decree, and sign it, so that it cannot be changed, according to the law of the Medes and the Persians, which cannot be canceled." The unsuspecting king was highly flattered by their request. He failed to observe that Daniel was not with the other presidents who stood before him. Not realizing what he was doing, the king signed the decree which was designed to destroy Daniel.

When Daniel heard that the decree had been signed, he went to his house. The window of his upper room opened toward Jerusalem. And he knelt before the window three times a day and prayed and gave thanks to his God, as he had always done. Then the evil men, who had been waiting for such an opportunity, came together and found Daniel on his knees praying to his God.

They hurried to the king and reminded him of the decree he had signed, and of the punishment he had ordered for anyone who disobeyed this law of the Medes and Persians. The king promptly agreed that the law he had signed must be upheld. Then the evil conspirators sprung their trap. They said to the king, "That Daniel, who is one of the captives from Judah, pays no attention to you, O king, or to the law that you have signed, but prays to his God three times a day."

The king, realizing how he had fallen into the trap, was greatly distressed when he perceived the wicked plot against his wisest and most trusted servant. He tried to think of some way to spare Daniel, and labored all day long to find a way to save him from the prescribed penalty. But when the sun went down, the cruel and hateful enemies of Daniel came before the king and declared that the law of the Medes and Persians must be enforced.

Then the king issued the fateful command, and Daniel was brought and thrown into the lions' den. But the troubled king said to Daniel, "Your God, whom you serve continually, will deliver you." And a great stone was brought and laid upon the mouth of the den, and the king sealed it with his own seal, so that no one would dare try to release Daniel.

Then the king went to his palace and spent the night fasting. He was unable to sleep, and no form of entertainment was pleasing to him.

The king rose very early in the morning and went in haste to the den of lions. When he came near the den where Daniel was, he cried out in a distressed tone and said, "O Daniel, servant of the living God, has your God, whom you serve continually, been able to deliver you from the lions?"

Then, from the stony prison, Daniel answered with a strong, clear voice, "O king, live forever. My God has sent his angel and has shut the lions' mouths, and they have not hurt me, because I was found innocent before Him; and also before you, O king, I have committed no crime." Then the king was exceedingly glad, and commanded that Daniel

The lions' mouths were shut and they did not harm Daniel

be taken up out of the den at once. So Daniel was taken up out of the den of lions, and no sign of harm was found upon him, because he had believed in his God.

Swift retribution fell upon those who had plotted against Daniel. The king commanded that the men who had falsely accused Daniel be brought and thrown into the den of lions. This was done; and they, their wives and children were thrown into the awful den. The fierce and hungry lions overwhelmed them

and broke all their bones in pieces well before they ever reached the bottom of the den.

Then King Darius wrote letters to the people of all nations, telling them of the wonderful way in which God had delivered his servant Daniel from the fierce and hungry lions. And he issued a decree that all the people in his great kingdom should reverence the God of Daniel. So this Daniel prospered during the reign of Darius and the reign of Cyrus the Persian.

SIXTY-EIGHT

Esther Is Made Queen

Esther 1:1–2:23

THIS is the story of how an unknown Jewish maiden by the name of Esther became queen of the great kingdom of Persia, during the time when many of her people, who had been carried into captivity, were still scattered throughout the empire.

Darius the Great had died, and his son Ahasuerus ruled over the vast kingdom of Persia which stretched from India to Ethiopia and which numbered over one hundred and twenty provinces. The old capital of Babylon had been destroyed, and the new capital of the Persian empire was Shushan.

In the third year of his reign, Ahasuerus made a great feast at his palace at Shushan to which he invited all of the princes, nobles, and governors of his provinces. The great feast lasted for six months, during which time the king showed the riches of his glorious

kingdom and the honor of his own majesty.

At the end of this time, the king gave a banquet which lasted for seven days, to all the people of the city of Shushan. The men were banqueted and entertained in the court of the garden of the king's palace, and at the same time Queen Vashti gave a banquet for the women in the palace.

On the seventh day of the banquet, when the king had become foolish and reckless from drinking too much wine, he commanded his servants to bring Queen Vashti before him adorned with her royal crown so that he might show the people and princes her great beauty. But according to the custom of that time, women wore veils over their faces, and were not supposed to be seen by men other than their husbands. So Queen Vashti refused to come at the king's command.

The king became very angry at Vashti's re-

Ahasuerus set the royal crown on Esther's head and made her his queen

fusal to obey his command. He wanted to punish the queen for her disobedience, and so he called together his wise men to ask them what should be done. Then the leader of them said to the king and to the princes, "Queen Vashti has done wrong, not only to the king but also to all the princes and people of the provinces of King Ahasuerus. For when this deed becomes known, women everywhere will look down on their husbands and will not show them the proper respect. Therefore let Vashti be queen no longer, but give her royal place to one who is better than she."

This counsel pleased King Ahasuerus and he decreed that Vashti could no longer be queen. Then, upon the further advice of his servants, he appointed officers in all the provinces of his kingdom to seek out beautiful young women and have them brought to the palace in Shushan. There they were to be placed under the custody of the officer in charge of the king's women, and prepared for presentation to the king. And the maiden that pleased the king the most was to be chosen queen instead of Vashti.

Now there was a Jew in Shushan by the name of Mordecai who had an office in the king's household. He had a young cousin by the name of Esther, whom he had raised from childhood, after the death of her father and mother. Esther was very beautiful, and Mordecai loved her as his own daughter. He knew that she would make a beautiful queen, and so he had Esther taken to the king's palace along with the other young women who were gathered there.

Esther immediately obtained favor in the sight of Hegai, keeper of the maidens; and he quickly provided her with the best of care and attention. Thus Esther was preferred above the others and given the best place in the house of the women. All this time she did not let it be known that she was a Jewess, because Mordecai had charged her not to make known her people. And every day Mordecai walked by the court of the young women, to find out how Esther was doing and what would become of her.

After twelve months of special preparation and beauty treatment, the maidens took their turns appearing before the king. When Esther's turn came, she prepared herself in the manner that Hegai had suggested. Esther was so beautiful that she found favor in the sight of all who saw her. So when she stood before the king, she found favor in his sight more than all the other maidens, and Ahasuerus loved Esther more than all the other women. The king set the royal crown on Esther's head and made her his queen instead of Vashti.

Then Ahasuerus made a great feast in honor of Esther to which he invited all his princes and servants. He also declared a holiday in his provinces, and bestowed gifts with royal generosity.

Mordecai could no longer see Esther every day as he had done before. But he walked by the palace and waited by the king's gate. One day when Mordecai was sitting at the king's gate, he overheard two of the king's servants plotting to lay hands on King Ahasuerus and kill him.

Mordecai immediately told Queen Esther about this evil conspiracy, and the queen revealed the matter to the king. Esther also informed the king that Mordecai was the man who had rendered this great service. Ahasuerus had the matter looked into, and the two men who had plotted against the king's life were both hanged. Then the record of Mordecai's warning and how he had saved the king's life was written down in the presence of King Ahasuerus in the Book of Chronicles.

Queen Esther's Noble Resolve

Esther 3:1–4:17

AMONG the princes at the royal palace of King Ahasuerus at Shushan was a proud and haughty man named Haman. He was wealthy and clever, and his driving ambition had won him great favor in the eyes of the king. In due time the king advanced Haman to a position above all his princes, and commanded all his servants to bow down in reverence to Haman.

Accordingly all the servants at the king's gate bowed to Haman when he passed by. But Mordecai would not bow to Haman. Being a Jew, he felt that such an act of reverence should be rendered only to God. His refusal displeased the rest of the king's servants, and they asked Mordecai why he dared transgress the king's command. Then Mordecai told them that he was a Jew, and that his religion did not permit him to show a man honor that should be reserved for God alone.

The servants then told Haman of Mordecai's unwillingness to bow down to him. Haman became furiously angry at Mordecai for his failure to do him honor, and he secretly determined to punish Mordecai. But, proud and haughty man that he was, he refused to lay hands on Mordecai himself. He decided he would have revenge against Mordecai by destroying all the Jewish people in the kingdom. At this time Haman did not know that Queen Esther was a Jewess and a cousin of Mordecai.

With great cunning, Haman contrived a plan to gain the king's consent to have the Jews put to death. He went before King Ahasuerus and said, "There is a certain people scattered abroad and dispersed among the people in all the provinces of your kingdom. Their laws differ from those of all other people, neither do they keep the king's laws; therefore it is not to the king's benefit to tolerate them.

"If it please the king," Haman continued, "let it be written that they may be destroyed; and I will pay ten thousand talents of silver to those who have charge of this business if they will bring it into the king's treasury." Ahasuerus did not know that Haman's plot was directed against the Jews; much less did he realize that his beloved Queen Esther was a Jewess. So in gross ignorance the king assented to Haman's evil plot.

The king gave Haman the authority to draw up an edict, embodying the sentence of death against the Jews, and to address it to the rulers in all the provinces of the kingdom. Hence letters were sent by special messengers to all the provinces, decreeing that on the thirteenth day of the twelfth month all the Jews were to be slain, young and old, women and children, and their goods to be confiscated.

Before long the news of this terrible edict reached the ears of the Jews in every part of the kingdom. They knew they had not done anything wrong, and they wondered why the king had decreed such terrible punishment upon them. The king and Haman sat down to drink in the palace, but the people of the city of Shushan were greatly perplexed at the sudden turn of events.

213

When Mordecai heard all that had happened, he was filled with dismay and grief. He tore his clothes, put on sackcloth and ashes, and went about the city, grieving with a loud and bitter cry. And in every province, wherever the king's command and his decree came, there was great mourning among the Jews. They all fasted and wept and wailed, and many of them lay in sackcloth and ashes.

When Esther's maids and servants told her that something was wrong, the queen was very upset. She sent clothes to Mordecai, so that he could take off his sackcloth, but he did not accept them. Then Esther sent one of her chief servants to Mordecai to learn from him what the trouble was all about.

And Mordecai told Esther's servant all that had taken place, and named the exact sum of money that Haman had promised to pay into the king's treasury for the extermination of the Jews. Mordecai also gave him a copy of the written decree that had been issued in Shushan for their extermination, and bade him show it to Esther and interpret it for her, and charge her to go to the king to make supplication to him and plead with him for her people.

Esther was deeply troubled by her servant's report, and she sent this message to Mordecai: "All the king's servants and the people of the king's provinces know that if any man or woman comes to the king in his inner court without being called, there is one law for all alike: they will be put to death, except such to whom the king shall hold out the golden scepter; he may live. But I have not been

Esther was deeply troubled by her servant's report

called to come in to the king these thirty days."

When Mordecai had received Esther's message, he bade the servants to take this answer to the queen: "Think not that in the king's palace you will escape any more than all the other Jews. For if you hold your peace at this time, aid and deliverance will come to the Jews from another place, but you and your father's house will be destroyed.

"And who knows whether or not you have come to the kingdom for such a time as this?"

Then Queen Esther sent Mordecai her great and noble reply: "Go, gather together all the Jews that are present in Shushan, and fast for me; neither eat nor drink for three days, night or day. I also and my maidens will fast likewise. So then I will go to the king, even though it is not according to the law; and if I perish, I perish."

So Mordecai went and did everything that Esther had commanded.

SEVENTY

How Queen Esther Saved Her People

Esther 5:1–10:3

ON THE third day of the period of fasting that Esther had arranged, she put on her royal apparel and went and stood in the inner court of the king's palace. The king was sitting on his royal throne, and when he saw his beloved Queen Esther standing in the court, she obtained favor in his sight, and he held out to Esther the golden scepter that was in his hand.

Then Esther drew near the throne and touched the golden scepter. The king spoke kindly to her and said, "What is it, Queen Esther? What is your request? It shall be given you, even to the half of my kingdom." Esther was not yet ready to disclose the full import of her request, so she graciously said, "If it seems good to the king, let the king and Haman come to dine with me today." The king gladly assented to this request, and sent word to Haman to invite him to the queen's dinner.

As they were eating dinner, Ahasuerus again asked Esther about her request, for he sensed that some matter of great importance was troubling her. Again Esther simply replied, "If I have found favor in the sight of the king, and if it please the king to grant my petition, let the king and Haman dine with me again tomorrow and I will tell the king my greatest desire."

Haman went home from the queen's dinner filled with joy and pride at the honor Esther had bestowed upon him. But when he passed Mordecai at the king's gate and saw that he still refused to bow to him, he was filled with indignation and hatred against Mordecai. But for the moment he managed to restrain his anger and contempt.

When he got home he called his wife Zeresh and his friends together, and boasted loudly about all the promotions and honors and favors the king and queen had bestowed upon him. But in spite of all these honors and rewards, Haman still bitterly complained about the way Mordecai, the despised Jew, had failed to pay him respect. Then his vengeful wife and all his friends urged him to prepare a gallows seventy-five feet high, and secure the king's permission to have Mordecai hanged upon it. This suggestion pleased Haman, and he had the gallows made.

That same night Ahasuerus the king could not sleep. To pass the time he commanded his servants to bring the book of the records of his reign, and to read them to him. Among other things, it was recorded how Mordecai had made known the plot of two men to take the king's life. The king had forgotten about this incident, but now he asked, "What honor and dignity has been given to Mordecai in reward for this service to the king?" The king's servants answered, "No honor has been given him."

At that moment Haman entered the outer court of the palace, intending to ask the king for permission to hang Mordecai on the gallows he had prepared. The king called Haman in and said to him, "What shall be done to the man whom the king delights to honor?" Haman thought to himself, "To whom would the king delight to do honor more than to myself?" So, believing that these honors were to be shown to him, he was ready with a very generous and elaborate proposal.

"Let the man whom the king delights to honor be arrayed in the king's royal apparel, and let him ride on the king's horse, and let the king's crown be set on his head. Let one of the king's most noble princes thus array the man, and escort him on horseback through the main street of the city, proclaiming before him, 'Thus shall it be done to the man whom the king delights to honor.'"

Then the king said to Haman, "Make haste, take the royal robes and the horse, as you have said, and do just that to Mordecai the Jew who sits at the king's gate. Omit no detail of all that you have described." So Haman, in great disappointment and resentment, took the royal robes and the horse, and arrayed his despised enemy Mordecai and escorted him through the main street of the city, proclaiming, "Thus shall it be done to the man whom the king delights to honor."

Then Mordecai went back to the king's palace, but Haman ran to his own home and covered his head in shame and sorrow. Haman told his wife and friends all the things that had befallen him, and how Mordecai had been honored by the king. They listened to his sad story and said, "If Mordecai, before whom you have begun to fall, is of Jewish descent, you will not prevail against him, but will surely fall before him."

While they were still talking with Haman, the king's servants arrived to escort him to the banquet that Esther had prepared. So the king and Haman went in to dine with Queen Esther. As they were dining, once more the king asked Esther about her petition. Queen Esther was now ready to tell her story, for this was the moment for which she had been waiting.

Then Queen Esther spoke fearlessly and said, "If I have found favor in your sight, O king, and if it please the king, let my life be given me at my petition, and my people at my request. For we are sold, I and my people, to be destroyed, to be slain, and to perish. But if we had been sold as slaves, I would have held my tongue; although our trouble is nothing compared with the loss that will come to the king."

Greatly surprised and moved by the queen's words, King Ahasuerus said to Esther, "Who is he, and where is he, that dares to do this thing?" And Esther indignantly replied, "The enemy is this wicked Haman." Then Haman trembled before the king and queen.

Esther indignantly replied, "The enemy is this wicked Haman"

The king rose up from the banquet in fierce anger, and went out into the palace garden to gain control of his thoughts. But Haman stayed to plead for his life from Queen Esther, for he saw that evil was determined against him by the king. The king returned from the garden into the place of the banquet just as Haman was pleading with the queen for his life. At the word of the king, Haman was seized and led out to be put to death.

One of the king's servants called attention to the gallows which Haman had prepared for Mordecai, whose word had saved the king's life. And the king commanded, "Hang him there." So they hanged Haman on the gallows which he had prepared for Mordecai. Then the king's fury was appeased.

After Haman's death, the king bestowed new honors and rewards upon Mordecai and exalted him to a position next in rank to the king. King Ahasuerus also gave Queen Esther and Mordecai authority to write and send letters to every province of the empire revoking the decree against the Jewish people. On the day appointed for the extermination of the Jews, they were given the privilege of defending themselves against those who would destroy them.

Therefore the Jews throughout the kingdom of Ahasuerus celebrated the day of their great deliverance with a great feast of thanksgiving, called the Feast of Purim. This Feast of Purim is observed to this day, and the Jewish people keep the holiday by retelling the story of beautiful Queen Esther, whose courage and devotion saved the lives of her own people.

SEVENTY-ONE

Nehemiah Revisits the Land of His Fathers

Nehemiah 1:1–2:18

NEHEMIAH was a Jewish nobleman of the captivity who was appointed to the hige office of cupbearer to the Persian king Artaxerxes. Nehemiah's position was a very important one. It was given only to some person who was altogether dependable and trustworthy. The cupbearer had to taste every cup of wine that was given to the king, so that no one would have a chance to poison the king.

Artaxerxes, the son of King Ahasuerus, began to reign in 465 B.C., and continued to rule until his death in 425 B.C. It was in the year 445 B.C., while Nehemiah was serving the king at the capital in Shushan, that the story of his great life work begins.

Some of Nehemiah's fellow Jews came from Judah to the capital at Shushan, and Nehemiah asked them about the Jews who had escaped captivity, and about Jerusalem. They reported to Nehemiah, "The survivors of the captivity there in the province are greatly afflicted and reproached; the wall of Jerusalem also has broken down, and its gates have been consumed with fire."

Nehemiah was terribly saddened to hear

this news, and he sat down and wept and mourned for many days. But he prayed earnestly to the God of heaven to give him the wisdom and strength to do something to help his people in their great distress.

One day as he was serving the king as cupbearer, the king noticed that Nehemiah's expression was very sad. The king said to him, "Why is your expression sad, seeing that you are not sick? This is nothing else but sorrow of heart."

Nehemiah was very much afraid that the king was displeased with him. So he hastened to tell the king of the heavy burden that was on his heart. He respectfully said to the king, "Let the king live forever. Why should my expression not be sad when the city, the place of my fathers' graves, lies waste and its gates have been consumed with fire?"

Then the king, showing real interest in Nehemiah's problem and welfare, said to him, "What do you request?" Nehemiah silently breathed a prayer to the God of heaven that he would find favor in the king's sight, and then he made known his request.

"If it please the king, and if your servant has found favor in your sight, let the king send me to Judah, to the city of my fathers' graves, so that I may rebuild it." The king graciously replied, the queen sitting beside him listening to Nehemiah's plea, "How long will your absence be, and when will you return?" Nehemiah stated that he would probably be gone a long time; but still the king was pleased to send him.

Then Nehemiah requested that the king grant him letters to the governors of the provinces beyond the Euphrates River, so that they would let him pass safely through to the land of Judah. He also asked for a letter to Asaph, the keeper of the king's forest, asking him to supply timber to build gates for the walls of Jerusalem, and for a house which Nehemiah would build for himself.

The king generously granted Nehemiah's request, and Nehemiah was thankful that the good hand of his God had blessed him in such fashion.

So, as the newly appointed governor of the province of Judah, Nehemiah set forth on his sacred mission. The king provided an escort of soldiers and horsemen to accompany him. He presented the king's letters to the governors of the provinces through which he passed, and these were properly honored. But some of the rulers near Judah, who were enemies of the Jews, were greatly distressed that someone had come to seek the welfare of the children of Israel.

After a long journey, Nehemiah reached the ruined city of his fathers, where he rested for three days. He did not tell anyone as yet the purpose of his visit, or what God had put in his heart to do for Jerusalem.

Then quietly one night Nehemiah took a few companions with him and rode around the city to see for himself the extent of the ruin and destruction. There was no beast with him except the one on which he rode. He went out by night by the gate of the valley and viewed the walls of the city which had broken down, and its gates which had been consumed with fire. In some places the destruction was so complete that he could not pass through on his beast. When he had completed his circuit of the ruined walls, he entered the city again by the gate of the valley.

The rulers of the city did not know where Nehemiah had been or what he had done. So far he had not told the Jews, the priests, the nobles, the rulers, or the rest of the people about his plan to ask their help in rebuilding the city's walls and gates.

When the right moment arrived, Nehemiah

called together the rulers and the people and said to them, "You see the distress that we are in, how Jerusalem lies waste and how its gates have been consumed with fire. Come, let us rebuild the wall of Jerusalem, so that we will no longer have to endure reproach." Then he told them how the hand of God had blessed him, and also how the king of Persia had aided him in his purpose.

Then the leaders and the people said, "Let us rise up and build." So they strengthened their hands for this good work.

Nehemiah rode around Jerusalem to see for himself the extent of the ruin and destruction

Nehemiah Rebuilds the Walls of Jerusalem

Nehemiah 3:1–6:15

UNDER Nehemiah's inspiring leadership and with the enthusiastic cooperation of the men and women of the Jewish community, the walls and gates of Jerusalem were quickly restored and rebuilt. Following a wise, sensible, and efficient plan of division of labor, all sections of the wall and all the gates were rebuilt by different groups of workers building simultaneously.

The high priest and his brother priests agreed to build the sheep gate and adjoining walls. Another group worked on the fish gate, and so on. But much to their shame and disgrace, some of the nobles of the Tekoites did not put their shoulders to the work. However, in spite of the shirkers, the work of restoring the walls and gates went forward. The old gate, the valley gate, the dung gate, the fountain gate, the water gate, and the horse gate were rebuilt and the doors, locks, and bars were set in. In like manner, the sections of the wall connecting the gates and towers were apportioned to the willing workers of many trades and crafts.

But the Samaritans and Ammonites, who were enemies of the Jews, were determined to stop the work of rebuilding if they could. Their leaders, Sanballat and Tobiah, tried every means they could think of to hinder it. First they tried disparagement and mockery. Sanballat said before the army of Samaria, "What are these feeble Jews doing? Will they make themselves secure? Will they revive the stones out of the heaps of the rubbish which are burned?"

Then Tobiah made fun of the Jews, saying, "Yes, the kind of wall they are building, if a fox climbed up on it he would break down their stone wall."

But Nehemiah and his workers were not deterred by these gibes and jeers of their enemies. Nehemiah prayed to God for strength and courage, and asked God to punish those who were trying to hinder the Lord's work. So the taunts and reproaches of the mockers were drowned out by the busy hum of the workers upon the walls. And soon Nehemiah was able to say, "So we went on building the wall; and the whole wall was joined together to half its height: for the people had a mind to work."

Next Sanballat, Tobiah, and their followers planned to attack Jerusalem and cause panic among the builders. When Nehemiah learned of this plot, he led the people in prayer to God for protection. He also set an armed guard on the unfinished walls as a protection against a surprise attack. In the lower places behind the wall, and on the higher places out in the open, he posted the people by families, with their swords, spears, and bows. Then Nehemiah said to the nobles, rulers, and all the people, "Do not be afraid of them. Remember the Lord, who is terrible and great, and fight for your brothers, your sons, your daughters, your wives, and your houses."

When the enemy learned that their plot was

known to the Jews, and that God had nullified their evil plan, the people returned to the wall, each to his own work. From that time on, half of them worked on the building, and half stood guard with spears, shields, bows and armor.

Those who worked on the wall and those who carried burdens labored in such a way that everyone worked with one of his hands while the other hand held a weapon. And each of the builders had his sword tied at his side as he built. The man who sounded the trumpet stood beside Nehemiah, ready to spread the alarm if the enemy appeared.

So the leaders and the people labored at the work, half of them holding spears from the break of dawn till the stars came out. Ne-

hemiah also instructed the people who lived outside the walls of the city, "Let everyone with his servant lodge within Jerusalem, so that during the night they may be a guard for us and labor during the day." So Nehemiah, his servants, and his guardsmen maintained their vigil night and day; they did not even take off their clothes at night.

Sanballat, Tobiah, and Geshem next formed a plot to kill Nehemiah. They invited him to hold a council with them in one of the villages in the plain of Ono. But Nehemiah realized their evil intention, and sent messengers to them, saying, "I am involved in a great task, so that I cannot come down. Why should the work stop while I leave it and come down to you?"

The walls and gates of Jerusalem were quickly restored and rebuilt

When this evil plot failed, these same men tried to slander Nehemiah. They wrote letters falsely accusing him and his people of rebelling against the king of Persia, and of planning to set up Nehemiah as king in Judah. But Nehemiah quickly told them that these charges were untrue; that they were lies devised to scare the Jews.

Finally they tried to induce Nehemiah to take refuge in the temple of God, saying that his life was in danger. They wanted him to do this so that they might accuse him of cowardice, and discredit him in the eyes of the people. But Nehemiah boldly replied, "Should such a man as I flee? And what man such as I would go into the temple to save his life? I will not go in." Then he prayed that God would judge these wicked men.

In spite of all difficulties, obstacles, and opposition from without and within, the work of rebuilding went steadily forward to completion. In the remarkably short space of fifty-two days the great project of restoration was completed.

FROM THE NEW TESTAMENT

*The Sermon
on the Mount*

I.

THE

FOUR

GOSPELS

The shepherds looked with wonder and adoration upon the baby Jesus

ONE

The Saviour Is Born in Bethlehem

Luke 2:1–20

THE Gospel of Luke has been called "the most beautiful book in the world." The story of the Saviour's birth is told only by Luke and by Matthew. Luke tells the simple and hallowed story of the coming of the shepherds to the manger where the newborn Baby lay. Matthew relates the strange and mysterious story of the Wise Men from the East who found the Christ Child in a humble home in Bethlehem. These two stories together tell of the wonderful miracle that is Christmas.

Luke first of all relates how the angel Gabriel announced to the priest Zacharias that a son was to be born to his wife Elisabeth. Then he tells how this same angel appeared to Mary at her home in Nazareth and announced to her that she was to become the mother of the Son of God. Luke then describes the visit of Mary to Elisabeth, tells of the birth of John the Baptist, and records the songs of praise and blessing uttered by Mary and by Zacharias. He gives a glimpse of the childhood of John the Baptist, and describes his mission as the forerunner of Jesus, the Messiah. Then he gives the story of the birth of Jesus.

In those days, the Roman emperor, Caesar Augustus, sent out a decree that all the subjects of the Roman Empire should be enrolled in a census for the purpose of paying taxes. This particular census was made when Cyrenius was governor of the land of Syria. The decree required the Jewish people, who were at that time under the rule of Rome, to go to their native towns and cities to be taxed.

This applied to a good man by the name of Joseph who lived in Nazareth of Galilee. Joseph was a descendant of the house and family of David, and as such he was required to go to the city of David—that is, Bethlehem of Judea. Joseph also had to take with him Mary, the young woman to whom he was engaged to be married, so that she, too, could be enrolled in the census. They were compelled to make the difficult and dangerous journey at this time, even though Mary, in fulfillment of the angel Gabriel's promise to her, was about to give birth to her Child. The journey from Nazareth, which they made by foot and by donkeyback, was nearly a hundred miles, and took several days. But they reached Bethlehem without any harm coming to Mary.

Very soon after the weary travelers arrived in Bethlehem, it came time for Mary to be delivered. The little town was filled to overflowing with the crowds of people who had come, as did Joseph and Mary, to enroll in the census. All the rooms were filled in the village inn, and in the homes of the people of Bethlehem. There being no room for Mary and Joseph in the inn, they were allowed to take shelter in a stable.

There in that lowly place, when it was her time to be delivered, Mary gave birth to her first-born Son, wrapped the baby Jesus in swaddling clothes and laid Him in a manger filled with clean straw.

While this divinely human event was

quietly taking place, unknown to the busy pilgrims in Bethlehem, another event was taking place in the starlit fields not far from Bethlehem. Out in these fields were some shepherds, who were keeping watch over their flock by night. Suddenly an angel of the Lord came to them, and the glory of the Lord shone in a great flood of light around them. Of course the shepherds were startled and frightened by this. Then the angel spoke to them and said, "Have no fear; for behold, I bring you good tidings of great joy, which shall come to all people. For to you is born this day in the city of David a Saviour, which is Christ the Lord." Thus the wondering shepherds were the first to hear the glad tidings of the Saviour's birth.

The angel then made it clear to the shepherds how they could find the newborn Saviour, saying, "And this shall be a sign to you: you shall find the Babe wrapped in swaddling clothes, lying in a manger." And suddenly there appeared with the herald angel a throng of the heavenly angels, praising God and saying, "Glory to God in the highest, and on earth peace and good will toward men."

When the choir of angels had gone away from them into heaven, the shepherds said to one another, "Let us now go to Bethlehem and see this thing which has come to pass, which the Lord has made known to us." And they hurried as fast as they could across the fields; and when they came to the inn stable, they found Mary and Joseph, and the Babe lying in a manger. They looked with wonder and adoration upon the baby Jesus, and repeated the things the angel had said to them concerning Mary's Child. Mary and Joseph and other Bethlehem folk who heard the shepherds' story marveled greatly at what they had to tell. But Mary, the happy mother, kept all these things and pondered them.

The joyful shepherds left the manger scene and returned to their sheepfolds and to their homes, glorifying and praising God for all they had heard and seen, even as the angel of the Lord had revealed it to them.

This, then, is the story of the first Christmas: the story of the virgin mother and her holy Child; the story of the lowly shepherds and the heavenly angels; the story of the Saviour's birth and the joy of salvation and hope that came to all the people.

TWO

Wise Men Find the Christ Child

Matthew 2:1–12

MATTHEW'S account of the Christmas story relates that when Jesus was born in Bethlehem of Judea in the days of Herod the king, a number of Wise Men from the East came to Jerusalem, seeking the newborn King. Who were these princely visitors from afar? A halo of mystery surrounds the Wise Men from the East, but it is perfectly clear that they came to the land of Judea on a heaven-inspired mission. They were probably Persian priests, Magi, the wise men, the seers of their land and time. They were star men, worshipers of light, astrologers and astronomers. Their contemplation of the starry heavens stirred their deepest religious feelings, for they regarded the stars as "the thoughts of the Eternal."

When the Wise Men arrived in Jerusalem, after their long and difficult journey across mountains, rivers, and deserts, they let it be known why they had come. They asked the question, "Where is He that has been born King of the Jews?" And then they said, "For we have seen his star in the East, and have come to worship him." They expected to find everybody in Jerusalem rejoicing over the birth of their King, but such was not the case.

When Herod the king heard the news the Wise Men brought, he was greatly troubled, because he thought a rival king had appeared to take away his throne. And soon all the city of Jerusalem was troubled too, because the people feared what the wicked Herod might do. Herod quickly called all the chief priests and scribes of the people to meet at his palace, and he demanded of them where the Christ their King was to be born.

The chief priests and scribes knew what their Scriptures said about the coming of Israel's King, but evidently they did not know as yet that Jesus had been born. Turning to their Scriptures they told Herod that according to the prophet Micah, the Christ was to be born in Bethlehem; for so it was written by the prophet:

"And you Bethlehem, land of Judah,
Are in no wise least among the princes of
  Judah;
For out of you shall come forth a Governor,
Who shall be shepherd of my people Israel."

Then Herod summoned the Wise Men in secret so that he might have a private interview with them. When they came before him he inquired of them exactly what time the star had appeared to them in their own country. And he sent them to Bethlehem, saying, "Go and search diligently for the young child; and when you have found him, bring me word again so that I may come and worship him also." Of course the cunning ruler did not wish to go and worship the Christ, but was really plotting how he might destroy Him. But the Wise Men were not deceived; they

231

The star came to rest over the place where the Child was

read Herod's evil intention in his face and manner and character. They were glad to leave his presence and be on their way.

Their journey from Jerusalem to Bethlehem was an easy and happy one. As they hurried on under the cover of darkness, lo, the star which they had seen in the East went before them, till it came to rest over the place where the Child was. When they saw the star, they rejoiced with exceedingly great joy. They were assured again that God was leading and guiding them safely to their journey's end.

Before long they arrived in Bethlehem and came to the very house above which shone the beacon star. And going into the house they found the Christ Child, with Mary His mother, and they bowed down and worshiped Him. And when they had opened the treasures they had brought with them, they pre-sented Him with costly and precious gifts, gold and frankincense and myrrh. From these three gifts that were offered, many infer that there were three Wise Men. Otherwise it is not said how many Wise Men there were.

Thus the Wise Men from the East who worshiped light, and who followed His star to the little town of Bethlehem, found the Christ Child—the Child Immanuel, which means "God with us." The newborn King they worshiped was none other than the Bright and Morning Star, the Sun of Righteousness, the Light of Men, the Light of the World.

The Wise Men did not need the star to guide them on their homeward journey. God spoke to them in a dream and warned them not to go back to Herod.

So they departed to their own country by another route.

THREE

The Boy Jesus in the Temple

Luke 2:41–52

SOMEONE has said that the boyhood of Jesus is like a walled garden from which but a single flower has been given. But this one flower is so fragrant that it fills the heart with longing to see more of that beautiful garden. Just one incident from Jesus' boyhood days has been preserved, and it is recorded only in Luke's Gospel. It is the story of the visit Jesus paid to Jerusalem and the temple when He was twelve years old.

At the age of twelve, a Jewish boy became a "son of the law" and was expected to observe its requirements. Among the things required were the pilgrimages to the temple at Jerusalem to attend the great national feasts, such as the Passover. Joseph and Mary were devout Israelites and it was their custom to go to Jerusalem every year to attend the Passover feast. So when Jesus was twelve years old they took Him with them on their annual visit to the Holy City.

The city was thronged with Passover pilgrims from all parts of the country. A large company of the relatives and friends of Joseph and Mary went with them, and the boy Jesus was free to mingle with the crowds of people. When the week-long feast was ended, the parents started on the return trip to Nazareth, not knowing that Jesus had stayed behind in Jerusalem. They took for granted that He was somewhere among the company of relatives and acquaintances. So they went a whole day's journey before they missed Him. They asked everybody in the company if they knew where Jesus was and, when they did not find Him, they hastened back to Jerusalem anxiously seeking Him.

After three days of frantic searching, they finally went back to the temple, and there they found Him. They were greatly surprised to see their young Son sitting calmly among the venerable teachers of the Law, listening intently to them and asking them questions. And all the people who were gathered around were astonished by His spiritual understanding and His knowledge of the Scriptures.

Joseph and Mary were naturally very much disturbed and upset over their missing Son, who had given them such cause for alarm. So His mother, in a tone of reproach, said to Him, "Son, why have you dealt with us this way? Behold, your father and I have been looking for you very troubled; for we thought some great harm might have come to you." And the Boy said to them, "How is it that you did not know where to find me? Did it not occur to you that I must be in the house of my Father?" These are the first recorded words of Jesus, and they tell us how He was already committed to the work which the Father gave Him to do.

The parents were not able to understand fully just what Jesus meant by His words, but they did know that their divine Son was sent into the world to do the will of His Father in heaven. They were so happy to have found their Son again, alive and unharmed, that they did not let this matter trouble them.

So the boy Jesus went back to Nazareth with His parents, and obeyed them in all things. His mother continued to wonder about His words to her in the temple, and treasured them in her heart. In the happy home at Nazareth, Jesus grew wise and strong and increased in favor with God and was greatly beloved by the people who knew Him.

The young Jesus sat among the teachers of the Law

FOUR

John Preaches and Baptizes Jesus

Matthew 3:1–17; Mark 1:1–11; Luke 3:1–22

IN the days when Pontius Pilate was governor of Judea and Annas and Caiaphas were high priests of Israel, a new prophet came preaching the word of God in the desert places of Judea. This holy man of God was John the Baptist, the son of Elisabeth and Zacharias. He had been born just six months before Jesus was born, and had lived in the desert regions until this time when he was thirty years old. John wore a robe made of camel's hair, and a leather girdle about his waist. His diet for the most part consisted of locusts and wild honey.

John knew that God had called him to preach the message of repentance and to announce the coming of Christ, the Messiah of Israel. The people were deeply stirred by his forceful preaching, and great crowds went to hear him from Jerusalem and Judea and all the region about the Jordan River. Many of the people, hearing his earnest message, confessed their sins and were baptized by John in the river Jordan.

When John saw many of the Pharisees and Sadducees coming to him to be baptized, he rebuked them because he knew they were not sincere. And he denounced them, saying, "O generation of vipers, who warned you to flee from the wrath to come? Bring forth fruit worthy of repentance. Do not think you are safe just because you are the children of Abraham." To the masses he said, "If you have two coats, give one of them to the person who has none; and also share your food with the hun-

gry." To the tax collectors, who were in the habit of robbing the people, he said, "Exact no more than you are told to exact." And to the soldiers he said, "Do not do violence to anyone, do not accuse anyone falsely, and be content with your wages."

Many of John's listeners, having heard that the Christ was to appear, wondered whether John himself could really be the Christ. But John quickly told them he was not the Christ, but that his part was to prepare for the coming of the Christ. John explained, "I indeed baptize you with water; but One mightier than I is coming, the thong of whose sandals I am unworthy to loosen; He will baptize you with the Holy Spirit and with fire. His winnowing fan is in his hand, and he will thoroughly cleanse his threshing floor and gather the wheat into his storehouse, but the chaff he will burn with unquenchable fire."

One day while John was preaching and baptizing at the river Jordan, he looked up to see the Man from Galilee coming toward him. It was none other than Jesus the Christ, about whose coming John had been telling the people. Jesus spoke to John and asked to be baptized. But John knew at once that Jesus did not need to be baptized, and so he said to Jesus, "I need to be baptized by you, rather than to have you come to me to be baptized." Jesus answered John, "Let it be so now; for it is right for me to be baptized in order that I may do the Father's will." By this Jesus meant that it was necessary for Him to be united in

Crowds went to hear John

baptism with the people He came to save. Then John agreed to baptize Jesus. Immediately something remarkable took place. As Jesus was baptized and as He walked out of the water, behold, the heavens were opened to Him and He saw the Spirit of God descending in the form of a dove and alighting on Him; and lo, there came a mysterious voice from heaven, saying, "This is my beloved Son, with whom I am well pleased."

The vision of the Holy Spirit as a dove was a symbol of the gentleness and lowliness of the life and ministry of Jesus. And the voice of the heavenly Father was the sign declaring Jesus to be the promised Messiah, the very Christ of God. John the Baptist knew this to be the case and declared, "I have seen and have testified that this is the Son of God."

FIVE

Jesus' Temptation in the Wilderness

Matthew 4:1–11; Mark 1:12–13; Luke 4:1–13

AFTER His baptism by John, Jesus, full of the Holy Spirit, returned from the Jordan and was led by the Spirit into the wilderness. He remained there forty days, spending the time in fasting, meditation, and prayer. During all this time he ate nothing, and at the end of the forty days was ravenously hungry.

While He was in this faint and starving condition, Satan, the evil spirit, came to Him and tempted Him, saying, "If you are really the Son of God, command this stone to become bread and satisfy your hunger." But Jesus knew it was not right for Him to use His divine power for selfish purposes, so He answered the Tempter, "It is written, 'Man shall not live by bread alone, but by every word that proceeds from the mouth of God.'" By this Jesus meant that those who keep God's commandments will have their needs supplied.

Then the Devil tried to tempt Jesus again.

He took Him to the city of Jerusalem, and set Him on the highest tower of the temple, and said to Him, "If you are indeed the Son of God, hurl yourself down from here and prove that God will not let you be hurt. Surely you believe God's word that says, 'He will put you in the charge of His angels'; and 'In their hands they will bear you up, lest at any time you should dash your foot against a stone.'" But Jesus was not deceived by the Tempter's false and cunning use of the Scriptures. He replied with the right and true meaning of God's word, saying, "Again it is written, 'You shall not make trial of the Lord your God.'" He meant that God's children should never doubt His goodness, but should always trust in His providential care and keeping.

Still the Devil was not satisfied, and tried a third time to tempt Jesus to disobey the Father's will and purpose for Him. This time Satan took Him to a very high mountain, and caused a vision of all the kingdoms of the world and their glory to pass before His eyes. Satan claimed that all these earthly kingdoms belonged to him, and that it was in his power to give them to Jesus. "I will give you all these," Satan lied, "if you will fall down and worship me." But Jesus was not deceived for a moment. He knew that it was not God's will for Him to build His kingdom by making any kind of bargain or compromise with the wicked Prince of this world. So again relying upon the truth and guidance of God's word, Jesus rejected this temptation, saying, "Go from here, Satan; for it is written, 'You shall worship the Lord your God, and him only shall you serve.'"

The Devil, having ended every temptation, and seeing that he had no power at all over Jesus, departed from Him, until a more opportune time should come.

Then the loving heavenly Father, approving the obedience, trust, and complete consecration of His Son, sent His holy angels to minister to Him and to care for His every need.

Jesus remained in the wilderness for forty days

Jesus said, "Fill the vessels with water"

SIX

Jesus' First Miracle

John 2:1–11

Jesus' first miracle was performed at a wedding feast in Cana of Galilee, a town situated about four miles from Nazareth where Jesus was brought up. Jesus, His mother Mary, and a number of His disciples were invited to the wedding.

Before the wedding feast was over, all the wine had been used, and there was no more for the guests to drink. Mary was greatly disturbed that this should happen.

So she went to Jesus, thinking that He would somehow be able to help, and said to Him, "They have no wine."

But Jesus answered Mary, "Woman, what have I to do with that? My hour has not yet come."

Still Mary knew that Jesus was willing to help in the emergency, so she told the servants to do whatever He asked them to do. In the dining room were six large stone vessels, now empty but capable of holding about twenty-five gallons of water each. It was the custom to pour water out of these vessels into basins in order to wash the dust from the feet of the guests. Jesus said to the servants, "Fill the vessels with water." When they had filled them, He said, "Now draw out some of the liquid, and take it to the ruler of the feast."

As the servants drew the liquid out of the vessels, they were amazed to see that the water had been turned into wine! They took it to the ruler, who was unaware of the miracle that had taken place. When he tasted the wine, he found it so excellent that he called the bridegroom and said to him, "Every man sets forth good wine at the beginning; and when men have drunk liberally, then the inferior wine; but you have kept the good wine until now."

The changing of the water into wine was the first miracle Jesus performed. The purpose of it was to show forth His power and glory as the Son of God.

SEVEN

Jesus Raises the Daughter of Jairus

Matthew 9:18–30; Mark 5:21–43; Luke 8:40–56

AFTER healing the man possessed with a legion of demons in the country of the Gadarenes, Jesus got in a boat with His disciples and crossed to the western shore of the Sea of Galilee at Capernaum. As soon as the boat touched the shore, a great crowd of people gathered around Jesus, for they were all waiting for Him. They wanted to hear more of His teachings, and to see more of His miracles of healing.

At once there ran forth from the crowd a man by the name of Jairus, a ruler of the synagogue, with a look of anxiety and distress on his face. He fell down at Jesus' feet and poured out his urgent plea: "My only little daughter is lying at the point of death. Come, Master, and lay your hands on her, so that she may be healed, and live." Jesus had compassion on this troubled father and started at once to go with him to his home.

But an interruption occurred. The crowd of people followed Jesus and thronged about Him. In this throng was a poor woman who had suffered from a dreadful disease for twelve long years. She had been to many physicians, but none of them had cured her. She had spent all her money, and her sickness had become worse instead of better. She had heard about Jesus' power to heal the sick, and she believed that He would be able to heal her. She thought she need only touch His garment to be cured. So she worked her way through the crowd and came up behind Jesus,

and with timid and trembling fingers touched the fringe of His garment. And immediately the flow of blood that had wasted her body ceased; and she felt in her body that she was cured of her illness. She thought she could slip away without anyone knowing what had happened. But she did not understand the nature of Jesus' healing power.

Jesus felt within Himself that healing virtue had gone out of Him, and He turned about in the throng and said, "Who touched my clothing?" The disciples thought this an absurd question, seeing that the people thronged on every side. But the woman, in fear and trembling, knowing what Jesus had done for her, came to Him and knelt at His feet, and told Him the whole truth. Then the Good Physician lovingly said to her, "Daughter, your faith has made you well; go in peace, and be cured of your illness."

While Jesus was still speaking to this woman, and while Jairus was anxiously waiting for Jesus to move on, a messenger came from Jairus' house with bad news, saying, "Your daughter is dead; do not trouble the Master any more." But Jesus, on hearing this, comforted Jairus by saying, "Do not be afraid; only believe, and she shall be well."

And when Jesus came to the house, He permitted no one to enter with Him except Peter and John and James, and the father and mother of the little girl. Jesus said to the crowd of mourners who were weeping and wailing loudly, "Do not weep; for she is not

Jesus said, "Arise"

dead but sleeping." But they laughed scornfully at Him, knowing that she was already dead.

Jesus put them all out of the house, and taking the child's parents and the three disciples went into the room where the beautiful little girl lay, still and white. Jesus took the little girl's hand into His own, and said to her in His own native Aramaic tongue, *"Talitha cumi,"* which means "Little maid, I say to you, 'Arise.' " And instantly the child got up and walked; for she was twelve years old. The parents were beside themselves with joy and astonishment at the recovery of their daughter. Jesus reminded them to give the little girl something to eat, for she was alive and well and hungry again. He also strictly charged them not to tell what He had done, for He wanted the people to know that His real work was to teach the truths of God's kingdom, and to give new life to the souls of men.

EIGHT

A Lad's Lunch and a Great Miracle

Matthew 14:13-21; Mark 6:30-44; Luke 9:10-17; John 6:1-14

THE disciples, having buried their friend John the Baptist, returned to Jesus and told Him all about their sad experience. Seeing that His disciples were weary and disheartened, Jesus gently said to them, "Come with me and we will go away to some quiet place and rest awhile." For many were coming and going, and they had no free time even to eat. So they all got into a boat and headed for a lonely spot on the northern shore of a lake, in the region of Bethsaida.

But the crowds of people saw them leave, guessed where they were going, and hurried to the place ahead of them. As Jesus stepped out of the boat, He saw a great crowd of people there to meet Him. Instead of being impatient with them, however, Jesus was moved by compassion for them, because they were like sheep without a shepherd. So again He spent the day, weary as He was, teaching them the truths of the Kingdom, and healing those who were sick.

Late afternoon came, and the people showed no signs of leaving. The disciples came to Jesus, reminded Him of the lateness of the hour, and urged Him to send the people away into the country and villages round about so that they might buy themselves some food. Jesus surprised and startled them by saying, "You give them some food to eat." But they quickly replied, "We do not have enough money to buy bread for this great number of people, even to give each one a little." Jesus calmly said to them, "How many loaves do you have? Go and see."

At this moment, Andrew spoke up and said, "There is a lad here who has five barley loaves and two small fish; but what are these among so many?" Jesus answered Andrew's question by saying, "Direct the people to sit down." The disciples proceeded to have all

Jesus gave the broken loaves to the disciples to set before the people

the people sit down in groups upon the green grass. So they sat down, by hundreds and by fifties, and with their garments of many bright colors they looked like plots in a vast flower garden. As they waited, their eyes were all fixed upon the scene of the young lad handing his lunch of loaves and fish over to Jesus.

Jesus took the loaves and fish into His hands, lifted His eyes to heaven in a prayer of thanksgiving, blessed the lad's simple offering, broke the loaves into pieces, and gave them to the twelve disciples to set before the people; in like manner He divided the two fish among them all. And all the men, women, and children in the vast throng ate of the loaves and fish until their hunger was abated. And the number of those who ate of the loaves and fish was five thousand men, besides the women and children.

When they had all eaten as much as they wanted, Jesus commanded His disciples, saying, "Gather up the broken pieces that are left, so that nothing may be lost." So the dis-

ciples gathered them up and filled twelve baskets with the fragments from the five barley loaves and the two fish which remained after the people had eaten.

When the people realized what a wonderful miracle Jesus had performed to care for their needs, they exclaimed, "This is truly the prophet that has come into the world." The happiest person in all that crowd of people was the little lad who had given his lunch to Jesus, that He might use it to feed them.

Following the miracle of the feeding of the five thousand, Jesus returned to Capernaum, and talked there to the people about the deeper meaning of what He had done. He told them that the physical bread which they had eaten was the symbol of the spiritual bread which He came into the world to bring. He urged them to seek for this, which He was able to give them. This is what Jesus said: "I am the bread of life; he that comes to me shall never hunger, and he that believes in me shall never thirst."

NINE

Jesus' Glory on the Holy Mount

Matthew 17:1–8; Mark 9:2–8; Luke 9:28–36

THE Transfiguration of Jesus took place about a week after Peter had confessed Jesus to be "the Christ, the Son of the living God," at Caes-

area Philippi. At this time, Jesus took with Him three of His disciples, Peter, James, and John his brother, and he led them up into a high mountain to pray.

Moses and Elijah talked with Jesus

As Jesus was praying, suddenly a most re-markable change came over Him. His face began to shine as bright as the sun and His garments became sparkling white. The drowsy disciples became fully awake and saw their Master with all the radiant glory shin-ing forth from him.

But that was not all. As the disciples watched, suddenly there appeared in this flood of glory two men from the unseen world whom they knew to be Moses and Elijah. These two great servants of God talked with Jesus about His coming death on the cross at Jerusalem.

As Moses and Elijah were departing, Peter said to Jesus, "Master, it is good for us to be here. Let us build three tabernacles, one for you and one for Moses and one for Elijah, so that they can stay with you here a while longer." Peter did not know what he was say-ing, because he did not understand the mean-ing of these strange events. But while Peter was still speaking, a bright and luminous cloud came over them all, and it frightened them. To add to the wonder of it all, a heav-enly voice came out of the cloud, saying, "This is my beloved Son, with whom I am well pleased; listen to him."

When the three disciples heard this voice, they were overcome with fear and fell to the ground and buried their faces in their arms. Presently Jesus came to them and touched them tenderly and said, "Arise, and do not be afraid." And when the disciples looked up, Moses and Elijah had disappeared, and they saw no one but Jesus.

The three disciples never forgot this experi-ence. John later wrote in his Gospel, "We be-held his glory, the glory as of the only begot-ten of the Father, full of grace and truth." And Peter wrote, "We were eyewitnesses of His majesty. For He received from God the Father honor and glory, when there came the voice to him from the excellent glory, saying, 'This is my beloved Son, with whom I am well pleased.' And this voice which came from heaven we heard, when we were with him in the holy mount."

TEN

Jesus' Parable of the Good Samaritan

Luke 10:25–37

THE Parable of the Good Samaritan is one of the most familiar stories that Jesus told. The occasion on which Jesus spoke the parable was this. A certain lawyer or scribe came to Jesus one day and asked Him a difficult question. The lawyer was a man trained to interpret and teach the law of Moses to the people. He really felt that he did not need any instruction from Jesus, but he asked the question for the purpose of puzzling and testing Jesus. The question the lawyer asked was this: "Master, what shall I do to inherit eternal life?"

Jesus thought He would let the man answer his own question, so He replied, "What is written in the law of Moses? What do you read there?" This was an easy question for the lawyer, and he readily answered, " 'Thou shalt love the Lord thy God with all thy heart, and with all thy soul, and with all thy strength, and with all thy mind; and thy neighbor as thyself.' " That was a very wise answer, and Jesus said to the man, "You have given the right answer; do this, and you will find eternal life."

The reply of Jesus stung the lawyer's conscience. He realized that he had not fulfilled this great commandment of the Law which he could repeat so well. So he attempted to excuse himself for his failure by asking Jesus another question: "And who is my neighbor?" Then Jesus related the following story which showed the lawyer, and which is meant to show anyone else who hears or reads it,

what it means to be a good neighbor to one's fellow men.

One day a certain man was going down the lonely and dangerous road from Jerusalem to Jericho. Suddenly a band of thieves sprang upon him, stripped off his clothing, attacked him with clubs, and ran away with all his belongings, leaving the poor man half dead by the roadside.

The man lay there wounded and helpless. Presently a priest, having finished his religious duties in Jerusalem, came down the road and saw the wounded man in his desperate plight. But not wishing to be delayed on his journey, he gave a quick glance at the helpless man and passed by on the other side of the road. A little later a Levite, another religious man whose duty it was to help the priests in the temple service, came by; but he also hurried along without stopping to help.

But by and by a Samaritan came riding along, and when he saw the wounded, half-dead man, had compassion for him, and quickly went to him and gave him first aid, using oil and wine to ease his wounds. Then he lifted the suffering man on his own beast, and walking beside him took him to a roadside inn not far away. He stayed with the man all night, caring for him as best he could.

The next morning, as he had to go on his way, he gave the keeper of the inn a sum of money and asked him to take care of the wounded man until he was well again. He as-

The Samaritan eased his wounds

sured the innkeeper that he would repay him any additional amount he might have to spend for the man's care when he returned.

When he had finished telling the story, Jesus said to the lawyer, "Now which of these three men, do you think, was a neighbor to the man who fell among the thieves?" The lawyer answered, "The one who showed mercy on him and helped him." Then Jesus said to him, "Go and do likewise."

ELEVEN

The Parable of the Prodigal Son

Luke 15:11–24, 32

JESUS the friend of sinners was teaching one day when a crowd of tax collectors and those whom the Pharisees called "sinners" drew near to hear Him. The Pharisees and scribes complained about Jesus' friendly attitude toward these outcasts and criticized Him openly, saying, "This man receives sinners and eats with them."

Jesus took this occasion to speak several parables which teach that God is a loving heavenly Father who forgives and restores the penitent sinner who seeks His pardon and mercy. The Parables of the Lost Sheep, the Lost Coin, and the Lost Son all tell how the loving heavenly Father yearns after His wayward children until they are safe in His care and keeping.

The Parable of the Prodigal Son is a profoundly human and moving story. A certain man had two sons; and the younger of them willfully and foolishly said to his father, "Father, give me the portion of your estate that belongs to me." The father, knowing that it was not the wisest thing to do, nevertheless divided his money equally between his two sons.

Very soon thereafter, the younger son gathered together all he had and journeyed into a far country, where he proceeded to spend his substance wastefully in riotous living. Almost before he knew it, he had spent everything he had, and he began to be in want of food, clothing, and shelter. His fair-weather friends all deserted him, and no one helped him in his distress.

Out of dire necessity he went to work for one of the men of that country, who sent him into his fields to feed his pigs. The wretched young man was so hungry that he even ate the husks intended for the pigs, as no one gave him any food.

At last, in his sad and pitiful condition, the prodigal son began to think of the good home he had left and of his kind and loving father. He realized how foolish he had been to leave all this behind. He knew that even his father's

The father's heart was filled with love and joy as he met his son

hired servants had plenty to eat and to spare, while he was starving in a pigsty far from home. As he was thinking thus, he made a very important decision. This is what he said to himself: "I will arise and go to my father, and will say to him, 'Father, I have sinned against heaven and before you, and I am no longer worthy of being called your son; treat me therefore as one of your hired servants.'"

And he started out at once to return to his father's home. But while he was yet a great way off, his father saw him coming; for he had been looking and longing every day for his boy's return. The old father's heart was filled with love and joy as he ran out to meet his son. Lovingly and tenderly he hugged him and kissed him. The tearful boy knelt at his father's feet and confessed, "Father, I have sinned against heaven and before you, and am no longer worthy of being called your son."

But he got no further. His father had already forgiven his penitent son, and he called out to his servants, "Bring forth the best robe and put it on him, and put a ring on his hand and shoes on his feet, and bring the fatted calf here and kill it, and let us eat and be merry; for this my son was dead and is alive again: he was lost and is found." And the whole household began to have a happy and joyful time.

The father gave his poor, ragged boy a royal welcome. He bestowed upon his hungry-hearted son all the love and tenderness of which his fatherly heart was capable. That, said Jesus, is the love and mercy which God the heavenly Father bestows upon each of His penitent, obedient children who returns to the Father's home.

TWELVE

Jesus the Friend of Children

Matthew 18:1–6, 10, 14, 19:13–15; Mark 9: 33–37, 10:13–16; Luke 9:46–48, 18:15–17

THE Gospel stories give two beautiful glimpses of Jesus as the friend of little children. The first scene is in a house in Capernaum; the second is by the wayside in Perea. These scenes, though few, are precious to the hearts of Christians the world over, because they tell about the Saviour who loves the children of all lands and races; about the Good Shepherd who gathers the lambs in His arms, and carries them in His bosom.

Soon after Jesus was glorified on the Holy Mount, He returned with His disciples to the city of Capernaum. On the way the disciples began to argue and quarrel among themselves as to which one of them was the greatest. Jesus heard them arguing, and decided they needed to be taught a lesson that would make them more humble and kind and unselfish.

So when they came into a certain house in Capernaum (some think it was Peter's house),

Jesus took the little children into His loving arms

Jesus asked the disciples, "What were you arguing about on the way?" They all kept still, because they felt guilty that they had quarreled with one another. Jesus sat down in the house and called the twelve to gather around Him. Then He quietly said to them, "If any one of you wants to be first, he must be last of all and servant of all." By this Jesus meant that the way of humble service is the way to true greatness. Then, wishing to give them an object lesson they would never forget, He called a little child to Him (he may have been Peter's own little boy), and put him in the midst of the disciples. He took the child in His arms and said to the twelve, "Whoever receives one such child in my name, receives me; and whoever receives me, receives not only me but also the Father who sent me."

Then Jesus added, "Truly I say to you, unless you change and become like little children, you will not enter the kingdom of heaven. Whoever humbles himself like this child, he is the greatest in the kingdom of heaven. Whoever offends one of these little ones who believe in me, it would be better for him to have a great millstone hung around his neck and to be drowned in the depth of the sea." Then the Master concluded, "Be sure you do not despise one of these little ones;

for I say to you that in heaven their angels always behold the face of my Father who is in heaven. Moreover, it is not the will of your Father who is in heaven that one of these little ones should perish." The disciples were very much humbled by this lesson, and tried to be more loving and kind to one another.

Some time later, on His last journey toward Jerusalem, Jesus came one day to a quiet and pleasant place in Perea, east of the Jordan. As He stopped there to rest and to teach the people, a number of young mothers brought their little children to Him, so that He might touch them and bless them. But the disciples rebuked these parents and tried to send them away. They evidently thought that Jesus was too busy to pay any attention to the children. But they were wrong.

Jesus was highly displeased with what the disciples were doing, and said to them, "Let the little children come to me, and do not send them away; for to the childlike belongs the kingdom of God." Then He said to all the people, "Truly I say to you, anyone among you who does not receive the kingdom of God like a little child shall not enter it." And Jesus took the little children into His loving arms and blessed them, caressing their heads with His gentle hands.

THIRTEEN

Jesus the Good Shepherd

John 10:1–18

AFTER He had healed and received the man who had been born blind, Jesus taught the people in Jerusalem the beautiful allegory of the Sheepfold and the Good Shepherd. He did this to rebuke the Pharisees for having cast out the poor man to whom Jesus had given sight; to encourage the man in his faith and trust; and to describe again the loving, saving ministry of the Son of man who came to give His life as a ransom for many.

It has been said that this story in John's Gospel is the New Testament version of the Twenty-third Psalm, the "Shepherd Psalm." David, a faithful shepherd himself, sang, "The Lord is my shepherd"; and Jesus, who was called "the Son of David," claimed to be the True Shepherd whom God sent to seek and to save the lost sheep.

The first scene is in the early morning when the sheep are being led out from the fold by the shepherd. Jesus said, "Truly I say to you, anyone who does not enter the sheepfold by the door, but gets in by climbing over the wall, that man is a thief and a robber. But the one who comes in by the door is the real shepherd of the sheep. The doorkeeper opens the door to him; the sheep hear and know his voice, and he calls his own sheep by name and leads them out to find pasture. When he has led out all his own sheep, he walks in front of them, and the sheep follow him, for they know his voice. The sheep will not follow a stranger, but will run away from him, because they do not know the stranger's voice."

The people did not understand this too well, so Jesus tried to make it plainer to them. He said to them again, "Truly I say to you, I am the door of the sheep. Those who have come before me and claimed to be the way to God have been thieves and robbers, but God's people did not heed them. I only am the true door into the sheepfold; and anyone who enters through me will be saved, and will freely go in and out and find pasture.

"The thief comes to the fold only to steal and to kill and to destroy the sheep. But I came so that the sheep may have life, and have it abundantly. I am the good shepherd. The good shepherd is willing to lay down his life for the sheep. But one who serves only for hire, and who does not own or care for the sheep, when he sees the wolf coming, runs away and leaves the sheep, and permits the wolf to seize and scatter them. Again I say, I am the good shepherd. I know my own sheep and they know me, just as the Father knows me and I know the Father. Knowing the needs of my sheep in this way, I am willing to lay down my life for them.

"And I have other sheep beside and beyond the fold of Israel, even the people of all nations. I must bring them into the fold also, and they will hear my voice. And there shall be one fold, and one shepherd.

"This is the reason the Father loves me as

Jesus the Good Shepherd

He does, because I lay down my life for all the sheep. No man can take my life from me, but I lay it down of my own will. I have power to lay it down, and I have power to take it up again. This commandment I have received from my Father, and I must obey His will."

By this Jesus meant that as the Good Shepherd He would lay down His life as a sacrifice upon the cross, and that He would take up His life again by way of His resurrection from the grave. All who believe in Him as the Saviour and Lord belong to the "one fold" of which He is the "one shepherd."

FOURTEEN

Jesus Raises His Friend Lazarus

John 11:1–44

JOHN, in his Gospel, records only seven of the signs or miracles of Jesus, and the last and greatest of all is the raising of Lazarus from the grave. Lazarus was the brother of Mary and Martha whose home was in Bethany. They were all dear friends of Jesus, and the Master often visited their home where He received a warm welcome and loving care.

One day when Jesus was a day's journey away from Bethany, in the region east of the Jordan, Lazarus became very sick. Mary and Martha were greatly concerned about their brother, and they hastily sent a messenger to Jesus with the word, "Lord, he whom you love is sick." They knew that Jesus would be able to help them in their trouble. When Jesus received the message, He said to His disciples, "This sickness is not to death; but for the glory of God, so that the Son of God may be glorified by it." But for some mysterious reason, Jesus stayed two days longer in the place where He was.

Then after that He said to the disciples,

"Let us go back to Judea again." The disciples tried to persuade Jesus not to go, because they were afraid of what His enemies might do to Him. But Jesus reassured them by saying that God would take care of Him as long as He was doing the Father's work and will. Then He explained to the disciples what He was going to do. "Our friend Lazarus," He said, "is sleeping, but I am going so that I may awaken him out of his sleep." The disciples thought Jesus meant that Lazarus was taking rest in sleep, and said, "Master, if he is only sleeping, he will get well." Then Jesus told them plainly, "Lazarus is dead." And He added, "I am glad for your sake that I was not there, so that you may believe. Now let us go to him."

So when Jesus came to Bethany, He found that Lazarus had lain in the grave four days. As soon as Martha heard that Jesus was coming, she hurried forth to meet Him, but Mary remained in the house. Martha immediately unburdened her heart to Jesus, saying, "Lord, if you had been here my brother would not

Before the astonished gaze of all, Lazarus came forth

have died. But I know that even now God will give you whatever you ask." Jesus consoled Martha by saying, "Your brother shall rise again." Martha replied, "Yes, I know he will rise again in the resurrection at the last day," but she was not fully comforted. Then Jesus spoke to her these great words of promise and hope, saying, "I am the resurrection and the life; he that believes in me, though he were dead, yet shall he live; and whoever lives and believes in me shall never die. Do you believe this?" Martha humbly replied, "Yes, Lord; I believe that you are the Christ, the Son of God, who should come into the world."

When Martha had said this, she went into the house and softly called her sister Mary, saying, "The Master has come and is calling for you." Mary rose quickly and went to Jesus. When she came where Jesus was and saw Him, she fell at His feet, saying to Him the same words that Martha had spoken: "Lord, if you had been here my brother would not have died." When Jesus saw Mary weeping, and her Jewish friends weeping with her, His spirit was moved and He was troubled, and He asked, "Where have you laid him?"

They said to Him, "Lord, come and see." And Jesus wept with Mary.

Then Jesus, His spirit again moved, came to the grave where Lazarus was buried. It was a cave, and a great stone covered the opening. Jesus commanded those who stood by, "Take away the stone." But Martha would have prevented them, saying to Jesus, "Lord, by this time his body will be decaying, for he has been dead four days." But Jesus reminded her, "Did I not just tell you that if you would only believe you would see the glory of God?"

So they took away the stone. And Jesus lifted up His eyes and prayed, saying, "Father, I thank you for hearing me. And I knew that you hear me always; but because of the people who are standing by I said it, so that they may believe that you sent me." When He had thus prayed, He called with a loud voice, "Lazarus, come forth." And before the astonished gaze of all, the dead man came forth, bound hand and foot with grave clothes, and his face bound about with a napkin. Jesus said to those who stood near, "Untie him and let him go." So Lazarus was alive once more and was restored to his sisters Mary and Martha, to live with them in their happy home.

FIFTEEN

Jesus Anointed by Mary of Bethany

Matthew 26:1–13; Mark 14:1–9; John 12:1–8

THE anointing of Jesus by Mary of Bethany has been called one of the most beautiful acts of love and devotion ever bestowed upon the Saviour. It shows what one of the loving friends of Jesus did for Him at a time when the chief priests and scribes were plotting to kill Him, and when Judas Iscariot was conspiring to betray Him.

Six days before the Passover, that is, on the day before Palm Sunday, Jesus came to Bethany and lodged in the home of His friend Simon the leper. Some time before this, Jesus had evidently cured this man of his leprosy, and Simon had become a follower of Jesus. Simon may have been a relative of Mary, Martha, and Lazarus, or possibly the husband of Martha. These friends at Bethany made a supper in honor of Jesus and in gratitude to Him for having raised Lazarus from the dead. Lazarus was there and Martha helped serve the fine supper.

While the meal was in progress, and the guests were reclining on couches around the table, Mary quietly entered the room with an alabaster box of ointment in her hand and stood beside Jesus. Breaking the alabaster box of precious and costly ointment of nard, she poured it lavishly upon the head of Jesus and also anointed His feet with the fragrant perfume. Then, unbinding her long tresses, she wiped the Master's feet with her hair. And the house was filled with the sweet smell of the ointment.

The disciples watched all this but did not approve of what Mary had done. They became indignant and began to criticize and find fault with Mary. They complained against her, saying, "Why was the ointment wasted in this way? For it might have been sold for more than three hundred pence, and the money given to the poor." And they spoke very unkindly to poor Mary. In all this unseemly conduct, Judas Iscariot, who was to betray Jesus for thirty pieces of silver, was the ringleader. John, the disciple whom Jesus loved, says that Judas spoke as he did, not because he cared for the poor but because he was a thief, and that he even stole money out of the bag which belonged to the disciples.

But Jesus rebuked these selfish men and put a stop to their ugly and unkind words, saying, "Let her alone; why do you want to trouble her?" He then commended Mary for her loving deed, saying, "She has done a very good thing for me." Then reminding these thoughtless men of His approaching sufferings and death, He solemnly said to them, "You will always have the poor with you, and you can do good to them whenever you wish; but you will not always have me."

Jesus continued to praise and commend Mary for the loving desire and wise perception that had led her to perform her selfless act. "She has done what she could," He said; "she has in reality come beforehand to anoint my body for the burial." Jesus meant that Mary had done not the least but the greatest

261

Mary of Bethany wiped His feet with her hair

work she could possibly have done. He thought of her deed as having special relationship to His coming death on the cross.

Jesus concluded His praise and commendation of Mary with a statement concerning the timeless and universal influence of her beautiful deed. These were His words, "Truly I say to you, wherever this gospel is preached throughout the whole world, what she has done will be spoken of as a memorial of her."

SIXTEEN

Palm Sunday—The King's Triumphal Entry

Matthew 21:1–17; Mark 11:1–11; Luke 19:29–38; John 12:12–18

PALM Sunday marks the day of the coming of the King. On this day, Jesus made His royal entry into the city of Jerusalem and presented Himself to the people as the Son of David and as the King of Israel.

On His last journey to Jerusalem, Jesus finally came, with His disciples, to the villages of Bethany and Bethphage, on the Mount of Olives, just east of Jerusalem. Here He made preparations for His dramatic entrance into the city. He sent two of His disciples, who are not named, saying to them, "Go into the next village, and you will at once find an ass tied and a colt with her. Free them and bring them to me. If anyone says anything to you, you shall say, 'The Lord has need of them.'" So those who were sent went to the village and found it as Jesus had said. As they were freeing the colt, its owners said to them, "Why are you freeing the colt?" The disciples replied, "The Lord has need of it."

Matthew notes that the manner in which Jesus planned His triumphal entry into Jerusalem was an exact fulfillment of the word spoken by the prophet Zechariah, saying:

"Tell ye the daughter of Zion,
  Behold, thy King cometh unto thee,
  Meek, and riding upon an ass,
  And upon a colt the foal of an ass."

The disciples quickly brought the colt to Jesus, as He had directed. Then some of the disciples put their garments on the back of the colt to form a cushion, and Jesus sat thereon. As the lowly procession started down the slope of the Mount of Olives, most of the crowd of happy pilgrims spread their garments on the road for Jesus to ride over. Others of the multitude cut branches from the palm trees and scattered them on the road. And the throngs of people that went before Him and that followed after shouted, "Hosanna to the Son of David! Blessed is he who comes in the name of the Lord! Hosanna in the highest!" This was a familiar prayer to God for deliverance based on the words of

The procession entered Jerusalem

Psalm 118:25–26. The word Hosanna means "save, we pray."

When the colorful procession with King Jesus at the head entered Jerusalem, all the city was deeply roused, and the people kept asking, "Who is this?" Some of the people in the crowd answered, "This is Jesus the prophet from Nazareth of Galilee."

And it came to pass that Jesus went into the temple of God and put out all those who sold and bought in the temple, and threw over the tables of the money-changers and the seats of those who sold doves. He rebuked these evildoers, saying to them, "It is written, 'My house shall be called the house of prayer; but you have made it a den of thieves.'"

Then the blind and the lame came to Him in the temple, and He healed them. But when the chief priests and the scribes saw the wonderful things that He did, and when they heard the children shouting in the temple, "Hosanna to the Son of David!" they were very angry, and said to Him, "Do you hear what these children are saying?" And Jesus said to them, "Yes. Have you never read the Scriptures which say, 'Out of the mouth of babes and sucklings you have perfected praise'?" And leaving these hard-hearted men, Jesus went out of the city and returned to Bethany to find lodging with His friends.

SEVENTEEN

The Last Supper in the Upper Room

Matthew 26:17–29; Mark 14:12–25; Luke 22:7–23; John 13:1–15

THE Feast of the Passover was instituted by Moses to commemorate the redemption of the Israelites from their bondage in Egypt. It reminded the people that when the first-born of the Egyptians were slain, the houses of the Israelites, where the blood of lambs had been sprinkled, were passed over by the angel of death. The Passover feast began with a sacrificial meal. A lamb was slain in the early evening, roasted whole, and eaten with unleavened bread and bitter herbs. This Passover had been kept by the Israelites from the time of Moses until the time of Jesus. The story of how this ancient Passover was fulfilled and how Jesus gave it a new meaning, so far as Christians are concerned, is told in the account of the institution of the Lord's Supper.

During the last week of His life (now called Holy Week) Jesus spent every day teaching in the temple, and at night He went out and lodged with His friends at Bethany. The Day of Unleavened Bread, or the Feast of the Passover, came on Thursday of that week. On this day the lamb for the Passover feast was killed and eaten.

When this sacred day came, Jesus sent the two disciples Peter and John, saying, "Go and prepare the Passover for us, so that we may eat it together." The disciples asked, "Where do you want us to prepare it?" Jesus answered, "Behold, when you have entered the city, a man will meet you there carrying a pitcher of water. Follow him into the house which he enters, and say to the owner of the house, 'The Master says to you, "Where is the guest room where I shall eat the Passover with my disciples?" ' And this man will show you a large upper room furnished; there make ready." The two disciples carried out these instructions, and found it just as Jesus had told them. And they made ready the Passover.

Now when evening came, Jesus came into the house and went up to the large upper room, where they found the Passover supper all ready. Jesus sat at the center of the table, and the twelve apostles took their places around Him. In earnest tones the Master said to them, "I have greatly desired to eat this Passover with you before I suffer; for I tell you I shall never eat it again until it is fulfilled in the kingdom of God." And as they were eating, Jesus became very sad and sorrowful and said, "Truly I say to you, one of you will betray me." And they too became sorrowful, and began to say to Him one after another, "Is it I, Lord?" Jesus answered, "It is one of the twelve, even one who is dipping bread in the same dish with me." He then added this solemn warning, "The Son of man indeed goes as it is written of him, but woe to that man by whom the Son of man is betrayed! That man would have been better off never to have been born." Judas, who was to betray Him, said, "Master, is it I?" Jesus replied to the guilty man, "You have said it." And Judas went out into the darkness of night.

As Jesus continued eating, with the eleven loyal disciples around Him, He took bread, and when He had blessed it, He broke it and said, "Take, eat; this is my body." And He took a cup, and when He had given thanks He gave it to them, and they all drank of it. He explained the meaning of what they were doing by saying, "This is my blood of the new testament, which is shed for many for the remission of sins." He was referring to His coming death on the cross, as the Lamb of God who takes away the sin of the world. Then He added this promise, "I tell you I shall not drink again of this fruit of the vine until that day when I drink it new with you in my Father's kingdom."

John's account of the Last Supper relates how, after supper was over, Jesus rose from the table, laid aside His upper garments, and took a towel and wrapped it around Himself. Then He poured water into a basin and began to wash the disciples' feet, and to wipe them with the towel with which He was wrapped. He came to Simon Peter, and Peter objected, saying, "Lord, are you washing my feet?" Jesus replied, "What I do you do not know now, but you shall know later." But Peter foolishly retorted, "You shall never wash my feet." Jesus answered him, "If I do not wash you, you have no part with me." Then Peter, ashamed and humbled, replied, "Lord, not my feet only, but also my hands and my head."

When Jesus had washed their feet, and taken His garments and sat down again at the table, He explained the meaning of what He had done to them, saying, "You call me Master and Lord; and you speak rightly, for so I am. If I then, your Lord and Master, have washed your feet, you also ought to wash one another's feet. For I have given you an exam-

Judas left Jesus and the eleven loyal disciples at the Last Supper

ple, and you should do as I have done to you."

So the Lord's Supper was instituted by Jesus. It is the memorial of the Saviour's atoning death on the cross. The bread is the symbol of His broken body. The cup is the symbol of His shed blood. The Lord's Supper is observed because Jesus said, "This do in remembrance of me."

EIGHTEEN

The Saviour's Prayer in Gethsemane

Matthew 26:36–46; Mark 14:32–42; Luke 22:39–46

THE Garden of Gethsemane is remembered as the scene of the agony, the betrayal, and the arrest of the Lord Jesus. The name Gethsemane means "Oil press," and indicates that it was a garden of olive trees with an oil press for pressing oil out of the olives. The garden was situated on the western slope of the Mount of Olives, east of Jerusalem, across the brook Kidron. Gethsemane was a favorite sanctuary of prayer for Jesus when He was in that vicinity. He evidently went there again and again to pray, after His busy days of teaching and ministering in Jerusalem. For Luke says, "And he came out, and went, as was his habit, to the Mount of Olives."

Jesus and the eleven faithful disciples concluded their fellowship in the upper room with the singing of a hymn. The Master led the way through the deepening shadows to the Mount of Olives, and the disciples followed. When they came to the garden, Jesus stationed eight of the disciples at the entrance to keep watch, saying, "Sit down here while I go over there and pray."

Taking with Him Peter and the two sons of Zebedee, James and John, He went into the recesses of the garden. The Master began to be very sorrowful and heavy-hearted, and said to the three disciples, "My soul is exceedingly sorrowful, even to death; stay here and watch with me." The disciples were very tired and troubled, and did not seem to understand what the Master expected of them.

Jesus went a little farther into the depths of the garden and knelt down and prayed most earnestly, saying, "Father, if you are willing, remove this cup from me; nevertheless not my will, but yours, be done." Jesus was referring to the "cup" of His sufferings and death on the cross as the Bearer of the sins of the world. Although Jesus, in His human nature, shrank from the ordeal that lay ahead, yet as the Son of man and Son of God He submitted Himself wholly to do the Father's will.

Then He rose up from His prayer and came to the three disciples and found them sleeping. He said to Peter, "Simon, are you asleep? Could you not watch one hour? Watch and pray lest you enter into temptation; the spirit truly is willing but the flesh is weak." Again He went away, praying the same words a second time. And there appeared to Him an

Jesus prayed in the depths of the garden

angel from heaven, strengthening Him.

He returned a second time to the disciples and found them still sleeping, for their eyes were heavy. This time He did not disturb them, but leaving them again went away and prayed for the third time, using the same words. And being in an agony He prayed more earnestly; and His sweat became like great drops of blood falling to the ground.

Then for the third and last time Jesus came to the disciples and said to them, "Why are you still asleep and taking your rest?" It is enough; the hour has come; behold, the Son of man is betrayed into the hands of sinners. Rise up, let us go; behold, my betrayer is now at hand." Through the branches of the olive trees, Jesus could see the flaring torches of those who were coming to take Him.

The disciples failed to sympathize and watch with their Master during His hour of agony in Gethsemane, but He did not fail to watch over them. Having loved His own as the Good Shepherd, He loved them to the end.

NINETEEN

The Betrayal and Arrest of Jesus

Matthew 26:47–56, 27:3–5; Mark 14:43–52; Luke 22:47–53; John 18:2–14

WHEN Jesus had concluded His prayer in Gethsemane, and while He was still speaking to the drowsy disciples, the silence of the garden was shattered by the arrival of a motley throng of people. In this band of rough men were soldiers, captains of the temple, and representatives of the chief priests, scribes, and elders of the people. They were carrying torches and lanterns, and were armed with swords and sticks. Judas was leading the procession, because he knew the place where Jesus often went with His disciples.

The Master, knowing everything that was going to happen to Him, took command of the situation. He went forth out of the shadows of the olive trees and said to the startled company, "Whom do you seek?" They answered Him, "Jesus of Nazareth." Jesus calmly said to them, "I am he." When Jesus said to them, "I am he," and when they beheld His face still marked with the bloody sweat of His agony, they were overcome with awe and fear, and stepped back and fell to the ground. When they had recovered somewhat, Jesus asked them again, "Whom do you seek?" And they said again, "Jesus of Nazareth." Jesus said, "I have told you that I am he; if therefore you seek me, let these men go their way."

Now Judas had agreed with the chief priests upon a signal, saying, "Whoever I shall kiss is the man; arrest him and lead him away safely." So he drew near to Jesus and said, "Hail, Master," and kissed Him on the cheek. This abuse of the sign of friendship stung the

Jesus stood before Annas

soul of Jesus deeply, and He said to the betrayer, "Judas, do you dare to betray the Son of man with a kiss?"

The band of soldiers then laid rough hands upon Jesus and arrested Him. Then Simon Peter, having a sword, drew it and with a wild blow struck the servant of the high priest, Malchus, and cut off his right ear. But Jesus restrained Peter with the command, "Put your sword into its sheath; shall I not drink the cup which my Father has given me? All who take the sword will perish by the sword. Do you think that I cannot pray to my Father and He will send me more than twelve legions of angels?" And He touched the ear of Malchus and healed him.

Then the Lord turned to the crowd and said, "Have you come out as against a thief with swords and sticks to arrest me? I sat daily with you teaching in the temple and you did not lay hands on me. But now this is your hour, and the power of darkness." He then added, "But all this has come to pass in order that the words of the prophets might be fulfilled."

Then all the disciples forsook their Master and fled. And a young man, some say it was John Mark, followed Jesus as they led Him away. The young man had only a linen cloth about his body, and when the enemies of Jesus tried to seize him, he left the linen cloth in their hands and ran away naked.

So the band of soldiers and their captain and the officers of the Jews bound Jesus and led Him away. First they led Him to the house of Annas; for he was the father-in-law of Caiaphas, who was high priest that year. It was this Caiaphas who had given counsel to the Jews that it was expedient that one man should die for the people. So they had conspired to put Jesus to death.

When Judas, who had betrayed Him, saw that Jesus was condemned, he repented and brought back the thirty pieces of silver to the chief priests and the elders, saying, "I have sinned in that I have betrayed the innocent blood." But they haughtily replied, "What is that to us? See to it yourself." And throwing down the pieces of silver on the pavement, Judas went out and hanged himself.

TWENTY

Jesus Before His Judges

THERE are two general phases of the trial of Jesus: the ecclesiastical trial before the Jewish sanhedrin, or council, and the civil trial before the Roman governor Pontius Pilate. There are four different stages of the trial, as Jesus was arraigned in turn before Annas, Caiaphas, Pilate, and Herod. The confused and swiftly moving events of that night of trial can best be understood if attention is paid to the various parts of the story in logical order. The trial of Jesus, the innocent Saviour, was an ordeal of indescribable anguish, suffering, and torture.

JESUS BEFORE ANNAS

John 18:12–14; 19–24

FROM the scene of His arrest in the Garden of Gethsemane, the Master was led by His captors to the house of Annas in Jerusalem. Late in the night, with His hands bound behind His back, Jesus stood before Annas the high priest. The high priest began by asking Jesus questions about His disciples and His teaching. Jesus boldly answered him, "I spoke openly to the world; I always taught in the synagogue and in the temple, where the Jews always go; and I have said nothing in secret. Why do you ask me? Ask those who heard me what I said to them; behold, they know what I said."

Despite this honest and respectful reply,

one of the officers standing by struck Jesus with his hand, saying, "Is that the way for you to answer the high priest?" Jesus answered this brutal man, "If I have spoken ill, bear witness to the evil; but if well, why do you hit me?" Annas then sent Jesus bound to Caiaphas the high priest.

JESUS BEFORE CAIAPHAS

Matthew 26:57–68; Mark 14:53–65;
Luke 22:63–71

IT WAS about daybreak when Jesus was brought before Caiaphas, in the council chamber, where the chief priests and scribes and elders had hastily gathered together. Now the chief priests and the whole council sought false witnesses against Jesus, so that they might condemn Him to death. Many witnesses came forward and brought false charges against Jesus, but these witnesses did not agree with one another. At last two came forward and falsely accused Him, saying, "We heard him say, 'I will destroy this temple that is made with hands, and within three days I will build another made without hands.'"

Then Caiaphas stood up in the middle of the council and asked Jesus, "Are you not going to answer at all? What is it that these men say against you?" But Jesus kept still and gave no answer. Again the high priest said to Him, "I command you, by the living God, to tell us

273

whether you are the Christ, the Son of God." Jesus replied to Caiaphas, "I am; and you will see the Son of man sitting at the right hand of power, and coming with the clouds of heaven."

Whereupon the high priest tore his robes and exclaimed, "He has spoken blasphemy! Why do we need any further witnesses? You have heard the blasphemy. What is your judgment?" And they all condemned Him as deserving to be put to death.

Then some of those present began to spit in the Saviour's face, and to cover His face, and to slap Him. And some of them said to Him in mockery, "Prophesy to us, you Christ! Who is it that struck you?" And the burly guards pounded Him with blows.

JESUS BEFORE PILATE

Matthew 27:1-2, 11-14; Mark 15:1-5;
Luke 23:1-5; John 18:28-38

WHEN morning came, all the chief priests and scribes and elders of the people took counsel together against Jesus to put Him to death. And when they had bound Him they led Him away and delivered Him to Pontius Pilate the Roman governor. It was very early when they came to the hall of judgment. The Jewish rulers themselves did not go into the judgment hall, because they did not want to defile themselves; they wished to be ceremonially clean to eat the Passover.

So Pilate went out to them and said, "What accusation do you bring against this man?" They replied, "If he were not an evildoer we would not have given him over to you." This reply made Pilate angry, and he said, "Take him yourselves then and judge him according to your own law." But the Jews warily replied, "It is not lawful for us to put any man to

death." John notes that this statement fulfilled Jesus' prediction that He would die on the cross, not by stoning, which was the Jewish method of putting one to death.

Then Pilate entered the judgment hall again and called Jesus to him. So Jesus stood before Pontius Pilate. Pilate asked Jesus, "Are you the King of the Jews?" Jesus answered, "Do you say this yourself, or have you heard others say it about me?" Pilate was irked by this reply, and demanded, "Am I a Jew? Your own nation and the chief priests have given you over to me. What have you done?" Jesus startled Pilate by saying, "My kingdom is not of this world; if my kingdom were of this world, then my servants would fight to prevent me from being given over to the Jews; but now my kingdom is not of this place." With a show of interest Pilate said to Him, "Are you a king then?" Jesus, seeking to win Pilate, responded, "You say that I am a king. To this end I was born, and for this cause I came into the world, that I should bear witness to the truth. Everyone that is of the truth hears my voice." But Pilate turned away, saying, "What is truth?"

Outside the judgment hall again, the chief priests and elders shouted their accusations against Jesus, saying, "We found this man perverting our nation, and forbidding us to give tribute to Caesar, claiming that he himself is Christ a king." But Jesus did not answer their lies. Then Pilate said to Him, "Do you not hear how many things they declare against you?" But Jesus did not answer Pilate either, not even to defend himself against one charge; so that Pilate was astonished.

Pilate silenced the crowd, and announced his verdict, saying, "I find no fault in this man." But they were all the more insistent, shouting, "He stirs up the people, teaching throughout all Jewry, from Galilee to this very city."

Jesus was again brought before Pilate

JESUS BEFORE HEROD

Luke 23:6–12

WHEN Pilate heard this, he asked whether the man was a Galilean. And as soon as he heard that Jesus belonged to Herod's jurisdiction, he sent Him over to Herod, who was himself also in Jerusalem at that time. Pilate thus wished to avoid making a decision as to the fate of Jesus, and tried to shift the responsibility to Herod.

So Jesus was brought face to face with Herod Antipas, the man who had put John the Baptist to death, the man Jesus had referred to as "that fox." When Herod saw Jesus, he was very glad, for he had desired to see Him for a long time. He had heard much about Jesus and was hoping to see some miracle performed by Him.

Herod asked Jesus a great many questions, but Jesus gave the wicked king no answer whatever. The chief priests and the scribes had followed Jesus to Herod's palace and they stood near by, vehemently accusing Him. Herod was greatly angered by Jesus' refusal to speak, and decided to punish Him. So Herod and his soldiers treated Him with scorn and insulted Him. Then, in mockery, Herod arrayed Jesus in a gorgeous royal robe and sent Him back to Pilate. And Herod and Pilate became friends that same day, for before they had been at odds with each other.

JESUS AGAIN BEFORE PILATE

Matthew 27:15–31; Mark 15:6–20;
Luke 23:13–25; John 18:39–19:16

WHEN Jesus was brought back to Pilate, the latter called together the chief priests, the rulers, and the people, and said to them, "You brought this man to me as one who has been perverting the people; and behold, I examined him before you and found no fault in him touching those matters of which you accuse him; no, nor yet did Herod; for I sent you to him and lo, nothing worthy of death was done to him. I will therefore chastise him and release him."

Now at the time of the Passover it was the custom for the governor to release for the crowd any one prisoner whom they wanted. They had at the time a notorious prisoner, by the name of Barabbas, a man who had been thrown into prison for starting an uprising in the city, and for murder. So when the crowd gathered and presented their request, Pilate said to them, "Whom should I release to you —Barabbas, or Jesus who is called the Christ?" For Pilate knew that it was because of envy that they had brought Jesus before him. Moreover, when he had sat down on the judgment seat, his wife sent word to him, saying, "Do not have anything to do with that righteous man, for I have suffered greatly because of him today in a dream."

But the chief priests and the elders got busy and persuaded the crowd to ask for Barabbas and destroy Jesus. The governor again said to them, "Which of these two should I release to you?" And they cried out, "Barabbas!" Pilate said to them, "What shall I do then with Jesus who is called the Christ?" They all shouted out, "Let him be crucified!" A third time he said to them, "Why, what evil has he done?" But they cried out all the more, "Crucify, crucify him!" And their voices won out.

So when Pilate saw that he could not prevail, but rather that a commotion was starting, he took a basin of water and washed his hands before the throng, saying, "I am innocent of the blood of this righteous man; see to it yourselves." And all the people answered, accepting the responsibility for Jesus' death,

"Let his blood be on us, and on our children." So Pilate gave sentence that their demand be granted. Then he released Barabbas to them, and having scourged Jesus, delivered Him to be crucified.

John's account supplies other details of this picture. The soldiers, John says, wove a crown of thorns and put it on Jesus' head, and put a purple robe on Him, and mocked Him, saying, "Hail, King of the Jews!" And they struck Him with their hands.

Pilate went out again and said to the people, "Behold, I am about to bring him out to you, that you may know that I find no fault in him." Then Jesus came out, wearing the crown of thorns and the purple robe. Pilate said to them, "Behold the man!" When the chief priests and the officers saw Him, they cried out, "Crucify him, crucify him!"

Pilate replied, "Take him yourselves and crucify him, for I do not find any fault in him." The Jews responded, "We have a law, and by our law he ought to die, because he made himself the Son of God." When Pilate heard these words, he was very much afraid.

And going into the judgment hall again, he said to Jesus, "Where are you from?" But Jesus gave him no answer. Pilate therefore said to Him, "You refuse to speak to me? Are you not aware that I have power to crucify you and power to release you?" Jesus calmly answered him, "You could have no power at all over me unless it had been given you from above; therefore the one who delivered me to you has the greater sin."

Then Pilate sought to release Jesus, but the Jews cried out, "If you set this man free, you are not Caesar's friend; whoever makes himself a king speaks against Caesar." When Pilate heard these words, he brought Jesus out and sat down on the judgment seat at a place called the Pavement.

Now it was the day of preparation for the Passover. It was about the sixth hour, or noon. Pilate said to the Jews, "Behold your King!" But they cried out, "Away with him, away with him, crucify him!" Pilate said to them, "Shall I crucify your King?" The chief priests answered, "We have no king but Caesar." Then Pilate gave Jesus over to be crucified.

TWENTY-ONE

The Crucifixion of Jesus

THE story of the trial of Jesus begins with His falling into the hands of His enemies at the time of His arrest in Gethsemane. The story of the crucifixion and death of Jesus begins with His being handed over to His executioners after Pilate had scourged Him.

THE SOLDIERS MOCK JESUS

Matthew 27:27–31; Mark 15:16–20

THE soldiers of the Roman governor took Jesus into the judgment hall, and they gathered the whole company of soldiers before Him. They stripped off His outer garments and put a scarlet robe on Him. They plaited a crown of thorns and put it on His head, and put a reed in His right hand. And they knelt before Him and mocked Him, shouting, "Hail, King of the Jews!" And they spat upon Him, and took the reed out of His hand, and struck Him on the head. And after they had thus mocked Him, they took the scarlet robe off him, put His own garments on Him again, and led Him away to crucify Him.

SIMON CARRIES THE CROSS FOR JESUS

Matthew 27:32; Mark 15:21; Luke 23:26

As they were leading Jesus away, they met a man by the name of Simon, from Cyrene, a city in North Africa, who was coming into Jerusalem from the country. So far Jesus had been carrying His own cross. But the soldiers laid rough hands on Simon, put the cross on his back, and compelled him to carry it after Jesus. Simon became a follower of Jesus, for Mark tells us that he was the father of Alexander and Rufus, two young men who were well known to the early Christian community.

THE WEEPING DAUGHTERS OF JERUSALEM

Luke 23:27–31

As Jesus was conducted by the Roman soldiers on their journey to Golgotha, a very large crowd of people followed Him. In this company were a number of young women of Jerusalem who were truly sorry for the Galilean, and who bewailed and lamented Him. For this they are often referred to as "the weeping daughters of Jerusalem." The Master

noticed these kind friends, and was comforted by their expression of sympathy.

Turning to them the compassionate Saviour said, "Daughters of Jerusalem, do not weep for me, but weep rather for yourselves and for your children. For behold, the days are coming when they will say, 'Blessed are those who never bore or nurtured children.'

"At that time they will begin to say to the mountains, 'Fall on us'; and to the hills, 'Cover us.'"

THERE THEY CRUCIFIED HIM

Matthew 27:33–44; Mark 15:22–32; Luke 23:32–38; John 19:17–24

WHEN they had passed outside the city wall, they came to a place called Golgotha, which means "The place of a skull." The soldiers offered Jesus vinegar mingled with gall to drink, to deaden His sensibilities. But when Jesus tasted it, He would not drink it. And they crucified Him, and sat down to watch over Him there. It was the third hour, or nine o'clock in the morning, when they crucified Him. Then two thieves were crucified with Him, one on the right hand and one on the left.

Then the uplifted Saviour, speaking His first Word from the Cross, prayed, "Father, forgive them; for they know not what they do."

When the soldiers had crucified Jesus they took His garments and divided them into four parts, one part for each soldier. But His undergarment was without a seam, woven throughout. So the soldiers said to one another, "Let us not tear it, but let us cast lots for it to see whose it shall be." This they did, says John, in fulfillment of the Scripture, "They divided my clothing among them, and for my garments they cast lots."

Two thieves were crucified with Jesus, one on the right hand and one on the left

As an intended insult to the Jews, Pilate wrote a title and put it on the cross. The title read, "JESUS OF NAZARETH, THE KING OF THE JEWS." Many of the Jews read this title, for the place where Jesus was crucified was near the city of Jerusalem; and it was written in Hebrew, and in Greek, and in Latin. The chief priests of the Jews did not like this, and objected to Pilate, saying, "Do not write 'The King of the Jews'; but that he said, 'I am King of the Jews.'" But Pilate refused their request, retorting, "What I have written I have written."

The people who stood watching and who passed by the scene of the crucifixion derided Jesus on His cross, wagging their heads and saying, "You who would destroy the temple and build it in three days, save yourself. If you are the Son of God, come down from the cross." And in like manner, the chief priests, with the scribes and elders, mocked Him, saying, "He saved others; he cannot save himself. If he is the King of Israel, let him now come down from the cross, and we will believe him. He trusted in God; let Him deliver him now, if He will have him; for he said, 'I am the Son of God.'" And even the thieves who were crucified with Him hurled the same insults.

THE PENITENT THIEF

Luke 23:39–43

LUKE alone gives the detailed story of the conduct of the two criminals who were crucified with Jesus. One of them railed at Jesus on the central cross, saying, "If you are the Christ, save yourself and us." But the other thief rebuked him, saying, "Do you not fear God, seeing that you are under the same condemnation of death? And we indeed justly, for we are being given the due reward for our deeds; but this man has done nothing amiss."

And then in a prayer of penitence and faith he said to the Saviour, "Jesus, Lord, remember me when you come into your kingdom." And the forgiving Saviour, hearing his prayer for pardon and mercy, replied, in His second Word from the Cross, "Truly I say to you, today you shall be with me in paradise."

HIS FRIENDS AT THE CROSS

John 19:25–27

SHORTLY after the penitent's prayer for pardon, there drew near the cross of Jesus five of His faithful friends. One of them was John, the beloved disciple, and the other four were women. Two of these were members of Jesus' family, namely, His own mother and His mother's sister Salome. The other two women were Mary the wife of Cleophas, and Mary Magdalene. The suffering Saviour was greatly comforted by their presence.

When Jesus saw His mother and John standing by His cross, He addressed to them His third Word from the Cross. To His mother He said, "Woman, behold your son." By this He meant that He was giving John to her as a son to take His place. To his beloved disciple, Jesus said, "Behold your mother." By this He meant that He was committing His mother to John's care. And from that hour the disciple took her to his own home.

THE DARKNESS OVER CALVARY

Matthew 27:45–49; Mark 15:33–36; Luke 23:44–45

NOW from the sixth hour, or noon, until the ninth hour, or three o'clock in the afternoon, there was darkness over all the earth.

And about the ninth hour Jesus uttered His fourth Word from the Cross, crying out with a loud voice, in His own native Aramaic tongue, *"Eli, Eli, lama sabachthani?"* that is, "My God, my God, why hast thou forsaken me?" This awful cry of loneliness and suffering was misunderstood by those who were near the cross. Some of those standing by, when they heard it, said, "This man is calling for Elijah." And one of the soldiers, feeling sympathy for the Master, ran and took a sponge, filled it with vinegar, put it on a reed, and gave it to Him to drink. But the rest of the crowd said, "Let us wait and see whether Elijah will come to save him."

THE SAVIOUR'S THIRST

John 19:28–30

JOHN relates that after this Jesus, knowing that all had now been accomplished in fulfillment of the Scripture, uttered His fifth Word from the Cross, saying, "I thirst." The soldiers had a vessel full of vinegar standing near; so they filled a sponge with the vinegar, put it on a plant called hyssop, and held it to His mouth. When Jesus had received the vinegar, He uttered His sixth Word from the Cross, saying, "It is finished."

THE DEATH OF JESUS

Matthew 27:50; Mark 15:37;
Luke 23:46; John 19:30

WHILE the four Evangelists describe the death of Jesus, Luke is the only one who records the seventh and final Word from the Cross spoken by the Saviour before He died. According to Luke, Jesus cried out loudly, saying, "Father, into your hands I commend my spirit." And having spoken this prayer of trust to His heavenly Father, Jesus bowed His head and gave up the ghost.

THE ACCOMPANYING EVENTS

Matthew 27:51–56; Mark 15:38–41;
Luke 23:47–49

THE death of Jesus on the cross was accompanied by certain strange and terrifying events. In the city of Jerusalem, the great veil hanging in the sanctuary of the temple was torn in two, from top to bottom, by some mysterious power. And there was a great earthquake, and the rocks were split asunder. The graves were opened, and many bodies of the saints that had been asleep arose and came out of the graves after Christ's resurrection and went into the holy city and appeared to many. At the cross, when the centurion and those who were with him keeping watch over Jesus saw the earthquake and all the things that happened, they were greatly afraid, and said of Jesus, "Truly this was the Son of God."

And all the people who had come together at Calvary to see the sight, when they saw all the things that had happened, beat their breasts in terror and remorse and returned home.

There were also many loyal and faithful women present, looking on from afar, who had followed Jesus from Galilee and who had ministered to His needs. Among these good women were Mary Magdalene, and Mary the mother of James and Joseph, and the mother of James and John, the sons of Zebedee.

JESUS' DEATH CERTIFIED

John 19:31–37

JOHN says that because it was the day of preparation for the Passover, in order that the bodies might not remain on the cross on the sabbath day (for that sabbath was a high day), the Jews asked Pilate to break their legs to hasten death, so that they might be taken away.

So the soldiers came and with their heavy mallets broke the legs of the two thieves who had been crucified with Him. But when they came to Jesus and saw that He was already dead, they did not break His legs. But one of the soldiers pierced His side with a sharp spear, and instantly there came out blood and water.

John affirms that he was an eyewitness of these things, and that he is giving a true report in order that others might believe. He also states that these things were done in fulfillment of two prophecies from the Scriptures. One of these was: "A bone of him shall not be broken." And the other was: "They shall look on him whom they pierced."

TWENTY-TWO

The Burial of Jesus

Matthew 27:57–66; Mark 15:42–47; Luke 23:50–56; John 19:38–42

THE Apostles' Creed says of Jesus, "He was crucified, dead, and buried." After the enemies of Jesus had put Him to death on the cross, the dead Saviour came once more into the hands of His friends. So it was that Good Friday, the darkest day in the world, came to a close with a bright and tranquil twilight hour. Three hours remained of the day on which Jesus died. The sabbath began at six o'clock in the evening.

As evening drew rapidly on, a kind man by the name of Joseph, from the Jewish town of Arimathea, came forward to render a beautiful service to the dead Saviour. Joseph was an honored member of the sanhedrin, or council; a good and righteous man, who had not consented to the decision and deed of the council in condemning Jesus to death. He was also himself seeking the kingdom of God, and was a disciple of Jesus, but secretly, for fear of the Jews. But now Joseph had the courage to go to Pilate and ask for the body of Jesus. Pilate wondered if Jesus were already dead; and calling the centurion to him he asked him whether Jesus had died. When the centurion told him that Jesus was dead, he agreed to give the body to Joseph.

Another secret disciple, Nicodemus, who had at first come to Jesus by night, also came and brought a mixture of myrrh and aloes, about a hundred pounds weight. These two generous men, assisted by other kind friends, took the body of Jesus down from the cross,

Jesus' body was laid to rest

and wrapped it in clean linen clothes with the spices, as was the burial custom of the Jews.

Now near the place where Jesus was crucified there was a garden, and in this garden Joseph of Arimathea had prepared his own new grave, which he had hewn in the rock, and in which no one had ever yet been laid. Thus, because it was the Jews' day of preparation for the Passover, and as the grave was close at hand, they laid Jesus there. They rolled a great stone to the entrance of the tomb, and went away. The women who had come with Jesus from Galilee followed, and saw the tomb, and how His body was laid to rest. Among these faithful women were Mary Magdalene, and Mary the mother of James and Joseph. The women returned to their homes, and prepared spices and ointments.

On the sabbath day they rested according to the commandment.

The next day, following the day of preparation, the chief priests and the Pharisees came together before Pilate and said, "Sir, we remember that that deceiver said, while he was still alive, 'After three days I will rise again.' Command therefore that the tomb be made secure until the third day, lest his disciples go by night and steal him away, and say to the people, 'He has risen from the dead,' so that the last deception will be worse than the first." Pilate granted their request, saying, "You may have your soldiers keep watch; go, make it as secure as you can." So they went and made the tomb secure by sealing the stone and by setting a watch.

TWENTY-THREE

The Resurrection of Jesus

OVER and over Jesus had foretold to His disciples that after He had been put to death He would rise again on the third day. And so it came to pass. God raised Him from the dead. Christ, the Prince of life, had power to take up His life again in resurrection glory. The same Jesus who was crucified, dead, and buried, presented Himself alive, after His passion, by many proofs, appearing to His disciples during the space of forty days, and speaking to them concerning the kingdom of God.

The actual resurrection of Jesus is not described. The Evangelists do not attempt to explain the manner in which Jesus rose from the tomb. They simply declare the resultant fact. No one saw Christ rise from the dead. While Annas and Caiaphas were asleep, and while Pilate was tossing on his troubled bed, the Son of God moved out into the world to be alive forevermore.

THE RESURRECTION NEWS

Matthew 28:1–8; Mark 16:1–8; Luke 24:1–10

WHEN the sabbath was past, very early on the first day of the week as it began to dawn, a number of the faithful women went to see the grave. The group included Mary Magdalene, Mary the mother of James, Salome, Joanna, and others who are not named. They took with them the spices they had prepared, so that they might anoint His body. As they walked along sadly in the dim light of early morning, they were saying to one another, "Who will roll away the stone for us from the door of the grave?"

When they drew near and looked, they were surprised to see that the stone had already been rolled away, for it was very large. And behold, there was a great earthquake; for the angel of the Lord descended from heaven and came and rolled back the stone from the door, and sat upon it. His demeanor was like lightning, and his clothing white as snow. At sight of him, the soldiers who had been set to watch the grave were filled with fear and trembling and fell down like dead men. The women went into the grave, but they did not find the body of Jesus.

The resurrection angel spoke to the frightened women and said, "Have no fear; for I know that you are looking for Jesus who was crucified. He is not here; for He has risen, as He said. Come, see the place where the Lord lay."

Then the angel asked, "Why do you look for the living among the dead? Do you not remember how He told you, while He was still in Galilee, that the Son of man must be delivered into the hands of sinful men, and be crucified, and on the third day rise again?" And the women remembered His words. Then the angel added, "Go quickly and tell His disciples and Peter that He has risen from the dead, and behold, He is going before you into Galilee; there you will see him. Lo, I have told you." So the excited women departed quickly from the grave with fear and great joy, and ran to tell His disciples the resurrection news.

PETER AND JOHN VISIT THE EMPTY TOMB

John 20:1–10; Luke 24:12

MARY MAGDALENE ran ahead of the others, and went to Peter and John, and said to them, "They have taken away the Lord out of the grave, and we do not know where they have laid him." Peter and John at once started to run to the grave. John, the younger man, outran Peter and reached the grave first. John stooped and looked into the grave and saw the linen clothes lying there, but he did not go in. A few moments later Peter came, and he went into the grave. Peter saw the linen clothes lying there, and the napkin, which had been wrapped around His head, not lying with the linen clothes, but wrapped up in a place by itself. Then John, who had reached the grave first, also went in, and he saw the same things and believed that his Master had risen from the dead. For up to this time the disciples did not know the Scripture, that the Christ was to rise again from the dead. Then Peter and John returned to their homes.

THE FIRST TO SEE HIM

Mark 16:9–11; John 20:11–18

MARY MAGDALENE had the unique distinction among all Christian disciples of being the first to behold and to converse with the risen Christ. Her memory is enshrined in the Gospel of Easter: "Now when he was risen early on the first day of the week, he appeared first to Mary Magdalene."

After Mary had reported her astounding discovery of the empty tomb to Peter and

John, she came back to the garden. After all the others had gone, she lingered in the sacred place absorbed in overwhelming grief. As she stood outside the tomb weeping, she stooped down and looked in, and saw two angels in white sitting where the body of Jesus had lain, one at the head and one at the feet.

The angels said to Mary, "Woman, why are you weeping?" Mary sadly replied, "Because they have taken away my Lord, and I do not know where they have laid him." When she had spoken thus, she turned around and saw Jesus standing near, but she did not know that it was Jesus. The Master spoke gently to her, saying, "Woman, why are you weeping? Whom are you looking for?" Supposing Him to be the gardener, Mary replied, "Sir, if you have carried him from here, tell me where you have laid him, and I will take him away."

These were the last words of hopeless grief that Mary ever uttered. For Jesus spoke her name, "Mary." She turned quickly and exclaimed in Hebrew, *"Rabboni!"* which means "Master."

As Mary fell at His feet and sought to embrace Him, Jesus said to her, "Do not touch me, for I have not yet ascended to my Father; but go to my disciples and say to them, 'I am ascending to my Father and your Father, and to my God and your God.'"

By this Jesus meant to say that He could not remain with her and His other disciples in bodily form, but that after He had ascended to the Father He would abide with them always through the presence of the Holy Spirit.

Mary Magdalene understood this, and found the words of her risen Lord to be true. She at once hastened back to the place where the disciples were and told them that she had seen the Lord. And she repeated to them the things Jesus had told her.

JESUS APPEARS TO THE OTHER WOMEN

Matthew 28:9–10

THE other women who had heard the resurrection news from the angel, and who had been commissioned by him to carry the message to the disciples, departed quickly from the tomb with fear and great joy, and ran to tell the disciples the news. And behold, the risen Lord met them on the way and said, "All hail." The women came up to Him and bowed at His feet and worshiped Him. Then Jesus said to them, "Have no fear; go tell my disciples that if they go into Galilee, there they shall see me." This was the second appearance of the risen Christ to His friends on Easter morning.

THE REPORT OF THE GUARDS

Matthew 28:11–15

MATTHEW relates that as the women were going to tell the disciples that Christ had risen, some of the soldiers who were watching the grave went into the city and told the chief priests everything that had happened. The chief priests assembled the other members of the sanhedrin, and when they had taken counsel, they gave a large sum of money to the soldiers and instructed them to tell the people, "His disciples came by night and stole him away while we slept." They also said to the guards, "If this comes to the governor's ears, we will take care of him and see that you don't get into trouble." So the soldiers took the money and did as they had been instructed. Their falsehood continued to be spread among the Jews for many years afterward.

The angel of the Lord rolled back the stone and sat upon it

THE WALK TO EMMAUS

Mark 16:12–13; Luke 24:13–35

In the late afternoon of that first Easter day, two of Jesus' disciples were on their way to a village named Emmaus, about seven miles from Jerusalem; they were talking together about all the things that had happened. While they thus conversed and speculated together, Jesus Himself drew near and went with them. But in some way their eyes were prevented from recognizing Him.

The risen Master said to them, "What kind of conversation is this that you are having with each other as you walk?" They stopped, and looked with sad faces at the Stranger. And one of them, named Cleopas, answered, saying, "Can it be that you are only a stranger in Jerusalem and do not know the things that have happened there these last few days?" The Visitor asked, "What things?" And they replied, "The things concerning Jesus of Nazareth, who was a prophet mighty in deed and word before God and all the people; and how the chief priests and rulers gave Him over to be condemned to death and crucified Him. But we had trusted in Him as the one who would redeem Israel."

Cleopas and his companion continued, "And besides all this, three days have passed since these things happened. Yes, and some of the women of our company, who were at the grave early in the morning, reported amazing news: they did not find His body. They came back saying that they had also seen a vision of angels, who said that Jesus was alive. Some of the disciples who were with us went to the grave, and found it just as the women had said; but they did not see Jesus."

Then the risen Lord said to them, "O foolish men, and slow of heart to believe all the words that the prophets have spoken, do you not realize that it was necessary for the Christ to have suffered these things and to enter into his glory?" And beginning with Moses and all the prophets, He explained to them in all the Scriptures the things concerning Himself.

When they drew near the village of Emmaus, He made as though He would go further, but they constrained Him, saying, "Stay with us, for it is toward evening and the day is far spent." And He went in to stay with them. And as He sat at supper with them, He took the bread and blessed it, and broke it, and gave it to them. And their eyes were opened and they recognized Him; and He vanished out of their sight. Sad and hopeless no longer, the companions said to each other, "Did not our hearts burn within us while He talked with us on the road and while He was opening the Scriptures to us?"

And they rose up that same hour and hastened back to Jerusalem. There they found the eleven gathered together, and those who were with them said, "The Lord has risen indeed, and has appeared to Simon." Then the two disciples joyfully related what had happened to them on the way to Emmaus, and how the risen Christ was made known to them in the breaking of the bread in their home.

JESUS APPEARS TO THE TEN

Mark 16:14; Luke 24:36–49; John 20:19–23

During the evening of that first Easter day, the disciples were gathered together in the upper room behind locked doors, because they feared the Jews. As they were excitedly talking about the Lord's appearances to Simon and to Cleopas, behold, Jesus Himself came and stood before them and said to them,

"Peace be with you." The disciples were startled, but Jesus said to them, "Why are you troubled, and why do doubts and questions arise in your hearts?"

Then the crucified, risen Saviour said to them, "Behold my hands and my feet and my side, that it is I myself; handle me and see; for a spirit has not flesh and bones as you see that I have." Then the disciples were glad when they saw the Lord. And Jesus said to them, "Do you have anything here to eat?" They gave Him fish which he ate.

Jesus said to the disciples again, "Peace be with you. As my Father has sent me, even so I send you." And when He had said this, He breathed on them, and said to them, "Receive you the Holy Spirit. Those whose sins you forgive, they are forgiven; those whose sins you retain, they are retained." In comforting tones He continued, "These are the words which I spoke to you while I was still with you, that all things must be fulfilled which were written in the law of Moses and in the prophets and in the psalms concerning me."

Then He opened their hearts to understand the Scriptures, and said to them, "Thus it is written that it was necessary for the Christ to suffer, and to rise from the dead on the third day; and that repentance and remission of sins should be preached in His name among all nations, beginning at Jerusalem. And you are witnesses of these things. And, behold, I send the promise of my Father upon you; but stay in the city of Jerusalem until you are provided with power from on high."

JESUS APPEARS TO THOMAS

John 20:24–29

JOHN tells us that Thomas, one of the twelve, called Didymus or "the Twin," was not with the disciples when Jesus first appeared to them on Easter evening. Thomas was the one disciple who had missed Easter. So the other disciples told Thomas, "We have seen the Lord." But Thomas stubbornly replied, "Until I see in his hands the print of the nails, and put my finger into the print of the nails, and thrust my hand into his side, I will not believe."

Eight days later, His disciples were again in the upper room, and Thomas was with them. The doors were barred, but Jesus came and stood before them and said, "Peace be with you." Then He said to doubting Thomas, "Reach out your finger and put it here, and see my hands; and reach out your hand and thrust it into my side; and be not faithless but believing." In that moment Thomas was won to faith. He had no thought whatever of carrying out his boast. The sight of his crucified Saviour and risen Lord was enough. Thomas threw himself at his Master's feet, exclaiming, "My Lord and my God." The last of the eleven apostles had been won to faith in the resurrection of Jesus. Then Jesus spoke the words of the Easter beatitude: "Because you have seen me, you have believed; blessed are they that have not seen and yet have believed."

JESUS APPEARS TO THE SEVEN

John 21:1–17

SPEAKING to His disciples on the night before His death, Jesus had said to them, "But after I have risen again, I will go before you into Galilee." On Easter morning the risen Christ said to the women, "Have no fear; go tell my disciples that if they go into Galilee, there they shall see me." In keeping with this divine instruction and command, the disciples returned to Galilee and waited at the appointed place of meeting.

Seven of their number were evidently in the

neighborhood of Capernaum, and may have been making Peter's house their headquarters. These seven were probably all fishermen disciples. Five of them are named: Peter, Thomas, Nathanael, and the sons of Zebedee, James and John. The other two may have been Andrew and Philip. Simon Peter announced that he was going fishing. The others replied, "We also will go with you." So they went out immediately, got into a boat, and fished all night long. But they did not catch any fish.

The seven fishermen were weary from their toil and discouraged over their failure to catch any fish. Then, just as the sun came up, the risen Lord stood on the shore; but the disciples did not know it was Jesus. He called to them, "Children, have you caught any fish?" In disgruntled mood they called back, "No." The Visitor said to them, "Try casting your net on the right side of the boat, and you will find some."

Willing to try once more, they cast the net as directed, and now they were not able to pull it in, there were so many fish. Then John, the disciple whom Jesus loved, said to Peter, "It is the Lord." When Peter heard that it was the Lord, he put on his fisherman's coat, for he had been stripped for work, and jumped into the sea and swam ashore. The other disciples came in the boat, dragging the net full of fish, for they were about a hundred yards out from the land.

When they disembarked, they saw a fire of coals on the shore, with fish laid out on it, and bread. Jesus said to the puzzled men, "Bring me some of the fish you just caught." So Simon Peter went back and pulled the net ashore, full of large fish, a hundred and fifty-three of them. And even though there were so many, nevertheless the net had not ripped.

When everything was ready, Jesus said to them, "Come, let us eat." None of the disciples dared ask Him, "Who are you?" for they knew it was the Lord. Jesus took the bread and gave it to the hungry men, and also the fish. This, says John, was the third time Jesus had appeared to His own apostles after He had risen from the dead.

After they had eaten, Jesus turned to Simon Peter and said, "Simon, son of Jonas, do you love me more than these?" Simon replied, "Yes, Lord; you know that I love you." Jesus said to him, "Feed my lambs." And He said to him a second time, "Simon, son of Jonas, do you love me?" Simon answered, "Yes, Lord; you know that I love you." Jesus said to him, "Feed my sheep." A third time Jesus asked the same question, "Simon, son of Jonas, do you love me?" Peter was grieved because He said to him the third time, "Do you love me?" And he said to Jesus, "Lord, you know all things; you know that I love you." Jesus said to him, "Feed my sheep."

This was the method Jesus used to remind Peter of his threefold denial of the Master, and to restore him again to the work of an apostle. The fire of coals on the beach served to remind Peter of the fire of coals in the courtyard of the high priest. The threefold command spoken by Jesus was to let Peter know that he was restored and recommissioned as an apostle of Christ.

THE GREAT COMMISSION

Matthew 28:16–20

AFTER this the eleven disciples went to a mountain in Galilee to which Jesus had sent them. And when they saw Him again they worshiped Him. But some still had doubts in their minds. And Jesus came to them and in simple tones of great authority spoke these words to His chosen apostles: "All power is given to me in heaven and in earth. Go therefore and teach all nations, baptizing them in the name of the Father, and of the Son, and of the Holy Spirit, teaching them to observe all things whatsoever that I have commanded you; and lo, I will be with you always, even to the end of the world."

TWENTY-FOUR

The Ascension of Jesus

Mark 16:19–20; Luke 24:50–53; Acts 1:3–12; 1 Corinthians 15:3–8

THE ascension of the Lord Jesus is the last appearance of the Christ after the resurrection. It marks the final appearance of the risen Christ to the eleven apostles, and likewise His final disappearance from their sight. He showed Himself alive after His passion by many proofs, appearing to His disciples by the space of forty days. Each of these appearances, mysterious in character and impressive in meaning, was followed by a disappearance, equally mysterious and significant. These re-

Jesus made His glorious entry visibly into heaven

peated appearances and disappearances were intended to prepare the disciples for the final separation, and to enable them to believe in the living presence of their Lord and Master, even though unseen.

On the day that He was received up, He led them out from Jerusalem until they were on the other side of Bethany, on the Mount of Olives. So when they had come together, they asked Him, "Lord, will you at this time restore again the kingdom to Israel?" Jesus said to them, "It is not for you to know the times or the seasons which the Father has set by his own hand." Then He added these words of promise and command: "But you shall receive power after the Holy Spirit has come upon you; and you shall be witnesses to me both in Jerusalem and in all Judea, and in Samaria and to the uttermost parts of the earth."

Then He lifted up His hands and blessed them. As He bestowed this gracious farewell benediction upon them, He parted from them and was carried up into heaven. From the sacred spot where He had begun His last triumphal entry into Jerusalem before His crucifixion, He thus made His glorious entry visibly into heaven. And while the disciples were looking upon His ascending form, a shining cloud received Him out of their sight.

As they continued to gaze into heaven as He went, behold, two men stood by them in white garments and said, "You men of Galilee, why do you stand gazing up into heaven? This same Jesus, who has been taken up from you into heaven, shall come in the same manner as you have seen him go into heaven." Then they worshiped their crucified, risen, ascended Lord, and returned to Jerusalem with great joy, and were continually in the temple blessing God. Mark adds that they went forth and preached everywhere, and the Lord worked with them and confirmed the Gospel by the miracles that accompanied it.

II.

THE

BOOK

OF

ACTS

There appeared to them divided tongues as of fire

TWENTY-FIVE

The Coming of the Holy Spirit at Pentecost

Acts 2:1–41

THE Feast of Pentecost was a very popular feast of the Jewish year, and the city of Jerusalem was thronged with pilgrims from regions far and near. The festival fell on the fiftieth day after the consecration of the harvest season by the offering of the sheaf of the first ripe barley. This gave rise to the name Pentecost, or fiftieth day. The day of Pentecost described in the Book of Acts came fifty days after the death and resurrection of Jesus, and ten days after His ascension. This particular Pentecost has been called "the birthday of the Christian Church," from the special event that took place on that day.

The risen Lord had instructed His disciples not to depart from Jerusalem, but to wait for the promise of the Father—that is to say, the baptism or outpouring of the Holy Spirit. Accordingly, when the day of Pentecost had come, the general group of disciples, including the women and Jesus' own mother and brothers, were together in one place. As they were waiting and praying, suddenly a sound came from heaven like the rushing of a mighty wind, and it filled all the house where they were sitting. This sound indicated the presence and power of the Holy Spirit. And there appeared to them divided tongues as of fire, in such a way that they rested on each one of the disciples. These luminous tongues were symbols of the fervent witness and testimony each was empowered to give. And they were all filled with the Holy Spirit, and spoke in other tongues, as the Spirit gave them voice.

At this time there were present in Jerusalem devout Jews who had come from many different lands. When they heard the noise of the mighty wind, many of them came together, and they were confused and amazed, because each one heard the disciples speaking in his own language. And they wondered, saying to one another, "Are not all these people who are speaking Galileans? And how is it that each of us is able to hear them telling in our own tongues the mighty works of God?" And all were bewildered, saying to one another, "What is the meaning of this?" But others who did not understand the miracle, mocking the earnest disciples, said, "These men are full of new wine."

But the apostle Peter, standing up with the eleven, boldly lifted up his voice and spoke to the great crowd of people: "Men of Judea and all who live in Jerusalem, let this be known to you, and give heed to my words. For these men are not drunk, as you suppose. But what you have heard is the fulfillment of the message spoken by the prophet Joel."

Then Peter preached the first Christian sermon on that day of Pentecost. He began by saying, "You men of Israel, hear these words: Jesus of Nazareth was a man approved of God among you by miracles and wonders and signs which God did through Him among you, as you yourselves know. This Jesus, who was delivered up in accordance with the definite plan and foreknowledge of God, you have taken and with wicked hands have crucified and slain. But God raised Him up, having loosed the pangs of death, because it was not possible for the Lord of life to be conquered by death."

Then Peter added, "We are all witnesses that God raised Jesus from the dead. Being therefore exalted by the right hand of God, and having received from the Father the promise of the Holy Spirit, He has shed forth this which you now see and hear. Therefore let all the house of Israel know with assurance that God has made that same Jesus, whom you have crucified, both Lord and Christ."

When the people had heard Peter's message they were pricked to the heart, and said to Peter and the rest of the apostles, "Men and brothers, what shall we do?" And Peter said to them, "Repent, and be baptized every one of you in the name of Jesus Christ for the remission of your sins; and you shall receive the gift of the Holy Spirit."

Peter continued, "For the promise is to you, and to your children, and to all that are far off, even as many as the Lord our God shall call." With many other words Peter testified and exhorted them, saying, "Save yourselves from this perverse generation." Then those who received his words were baptized. And that same day there were added to the fellowship of the Church about three thousand souls.

TWENTY-SIX

The Lame Man at the Beautiful Gate

Acts 3:1–19

FOLLOWING the day of Pentecost and the coming of the Holy Spirit, the apostles had the power to perform many wonders and miracles among the people. The healing of the lame man at the Beautiful Gate of the temple in Jerusalem was one of the most notable of these. It is an example of the way the living Christ continued to do His works of healing and mercy through His chosen apostles.

One afternoon about three o'clock the two apostles Peter and John went up together to the temple at the hour of prayer. Their way led through the gate which was called Beautiful. Just outside the gate lay a poor crippled man who had been lame from birth. He had never walked in all his life, and now he was forty years old. His friends carried him to this place each day so that he might ask alms of those who entered into the temple to worship. He believed that when the people saw him they would take pity and help him.

Seeing Peter and John about to go into the temple, the lame man, in his low pleading voice, asked them for some small gift of money. Peter and John stood still and looked in sympathy upon the helpless cripple. Then Peter, fixing his eyes upon the man, said, "Look on us." The lame man at once gave them his full attention, expecting to receive something from them. But at the moment he expected nothing more than some small gift of money.

Peter surprised him by saying, "Silver and gold I do not have, but what I have I give to you; in the name of Jesus Christ of Nazareth, rise up and walk."

Then Peter reached down and took him by the right hand and pulled him up. Immediately his feet and ankles received strength. And leaping up he stood and walked and entered the temple with them, walking and leaping and praising God. And all the people saw him walking and praising God, and recognized him as the one who usually sat and asked for alms at the Beautiful Gate of the

The lame man gave Peter and John his full attention

temple. And they were filled with wonder and amazement at what had happened to him.

While the grateful man held on to Peter and John, all the astonished people ran together to them at the place called Solomon's Porch. And when Peter saw them come together, he addressed the people, saying, "You men of Israel, why do you marvel at this, or why do you look so earnestly at us, as though by our own power or holiness we had made this man walk?" He then told them that the God of Abraham and of Isaac and of Jacob, the God of their fathers, had glorified His Son Jesus in the working of this miracle of healing.

Then Peter charged them with having rejected the Christ of God, saying, "But you denied the Holy One and the Just, and asked for a murderer, namely, Barabbas, to be granted to you, and killed the Prince of life." He further testified, "God raised him from the dead, of which we are all witnesses. And through faith in the name of Jesus, this man who was lame now walks and has been given this perfect soundness of body in the presence of you all."

Then Peter appealed to them, saying, "My brothers, I know that you behaved in ignorance, as did also your rulers. Repent, therefore, and be converted, so that your sins may be blotted out when the times of refreshing shall come to you from the presence of the Lord." And many who heard Peter's word believed; and the number of the men came to about five thousand.

TWENTY-SEVEN

Stephen—The First Christian Martyr

Acts 6:1–7:60

THE name Stephen means "a crown," and he was the first of the early Christians to wear the martyr's crown. Stephen was one of seven deacons chosen by the apostles to care for the poor and needy in the Jerusalem Church. He was a very good and generous man, a devoted follower of Christ; a disciple "full of faith and of the Holy Spirit." He was the first deacon in the Christian Church; the first of that great company of devoted men and women who have ministered to the poor and needy in the name and Spirit of Christ.

Stephen was also a preacher of exceptional ability and forcefulness, and a worker of great wonders and miracles among the people. He proclaimed the gospel of Christ with great earnestness and power and persuaded his hearers to give heed to his message.

But many of the Greek-speaking Jews disputed with Stephen, and became very angry when they could not answer his arguments. These stirred up the people and the rulers and turned them against him. They arrested Stephen and brought him before the council. They secured false witnesses who said, "This man has been speaking evil words against the temple and the law of Moses. We have heard him say that Jesus of Nazareth shall destroy this place, and shall change the laws that Moses gave to us." As Stephen stood up to answer his accusers, all present fixed their eyes upon him, and saw his face shining like the face of an angel.

Then Stephen began his notable defense. He spoke to the council concerning the great things God had done for the people of Israel in the past. He said, "Men, brothers, and fathers, listen to my words. The God of glory appeared to our father Abraham, and called him to go forth into a new land." He then summed up the history of God's dealings with the children of Israel. He reminded them how Joseph had been sold into Egypt by his jealous brothers; how Joseph finally became governor of Egypt; how he saved his people in time of famine, and graciously welcomed Jacob and his family when they came to sojourn in the land of Egypt. He told how God had raised up Moses to lead the people out of Egyptian bondage; how the people had rejected Moses as their leader, and had asked Aaron to make them a golden calf to worship. He reviewed the mighty works of Moses, David, and Solomon on behalf of the nation. Then he showed them how the Israelites had not been faithful to the God who had given them all their blessings.

Finally Stephen accused his hearers of being like their fathers in hardness of heart and unbelief. "You are stiff-necked people," he said; "you are hard-hearted and slow to hear; you always resist the Holy Spirit."

When they heard these things, they became furious with anger and gnashed their teeth against Stephen. But this righteous man, full

Stephen spoke to the council about God

of the Holy Spirit, looked up to heaven and saw the glory of God, and Jesus standing at the right hand of God; and said, "Behold, I see the heavens opened, and the Son of man standing on the right hand of God."

Then they cried out loudly, and stopped their ears, and rushed upon him with one accord. They dragged him out of the city and stoned him. And while they were stoning Stephen, he knelt down and prayed, "Lord Jesus, receive my spirit. Lord, do not hold this sin against them." And then he fell asleep.

TWENTY-EIGHT

Philip and the Ethiopian

Acts 8:1–8; 26–40

PHILIP was one of the seven men of good reputation, full of the Spirit and of wisdom, chosen to be deacons to care for the poor in the Church of Jerusalem. Following the death of Stephen, a great persecution arose against the Church in Jerusalem, and the Christians were scattered abroad into many regions and places. And those who were thus scattered went about preaching the word of God. Philip was one of these. He became an outstanding evangelist.

He visited the city of Samaria, preached the gospel of Christ to the people, performed miracles of healing and casting out unclean spirits, and baptized many who believed in Christ. As a result of his good work, there was great joy in that city.

When Philip's work in Samaria was done, the angel of the Lord spoke to him, saying, "Rise up and leave this city and go toward the south to the road that goes down from Jerusalem to Gaza." This was a road through a desert region, without villages or people. But Philip obeyed the word of the Lord and went until he came to this desert road.

It soon became clear to Philip why the Lord had sent him to this place. As he was walking along the desert road, he saw a splendid chariot drawing near. And behold, there was a black man seated in the chariot reading from a scroll. This man had come from the land of Ethiopia, in Africa. He was a nobleman of very high rank, a minister of Candace the queen of the Ethiopians, who had charge of all her treasure. He had come to Jerusalem to worship God in the temple there, and was returning to his homeland. As he rode along, seated in his chariot, he was reading aloud from the prophet Isaiah.

As the royal chariot drew near, the Spirit of the Lord said to Philip, "Draw near and join this chariot." So Philip ran to the nobleman, and heard him reading from Isaiah the prophet, and asked him, "Do you understand the words that you are reading?" The nobleman very humbly replied, "How can I, unless someone should guide me?" And he very graciously asked Philip to come up into the chariot and sit with him. The passage of the Scripture which he was reading was this portion of the fifty-third chapter of the prophet Isaiah:

"He was led as a sheep to the slaughter;
  And like a lamb dumb before his shearer,
  So he opened not his mouth.
  In his humiliation his judgment was taken
      away.
  And who shall declare his generation?
  For his life is taken from the earth."

The Ethiopian said to Philip, "Pray tell me, about whom does the prophet speak this, about himself or about some other man?" Philip knew that these words referred to Jesus, the true Lamb of God, who suffered and died upon the cross as a sacrifice for sins. So Philip started to speak, and beginning at this same Scripture he preached to him the story of Jesus. The black man eagerly took Philip's words to heart and earnestly believed in Jesus.

As they traveled along the road they came to a place where there was some water, and the nobleman cried, "See, here is some water. What should prevent me from being baptized?" Philip said to him, "If you believe with all your heart, you may be baptized." And the man replied, "I believe that Jesus Christ is the Son of God."

He then commanded the chariot to stand still, and they went down into the water, and Philip baptized the Ethiopian as a disciple of Christ. And when they came up out of the water, the Spirit of the Lord directed Philip to go on his way, and the nobleman saw him no more. But he went on his homeward way rejoicing because he had found the Saviour and had become a Christian.

Philip went on until he came to Azotus, on the shore of the Mediterranean Sea, where he also preached the Gospel. From there he traveled northward, preaching in all the towns along the coast until he came to Caesarea, where he lived for many years.

Philip preached to the Ethiopian the story of Jesus

TWENTY-NINE

The Conversion of Saul of Tarsus

Acts 9:1–30

THE first glimpse of Saul of Tarsus is a very forbidding one. He first appears in the record of the Book of Acts at the stoning of Stephen. In that sad story it is described how those who stoned Stephen laid down their garments at the feet of a young man named Saul, and that Saul was consenting to his death.

There followed a great persecution against the Church in Jerusalem; and all of the Christians, except the apostles, were scattered abroad throughout Judea and Samaria. And Saul, becoming the chief persecutor, made havoc of the Church, entering into every house and dragging men and women off to prison.

But Saul was not satisfied to confine his baneful activities against the Christians to Jerusalem. Still breathing threats and slaughter against the disciples of the Lord, he went to the high priest and requested letters to the synagogues at Damascus, over a hundred miles away, so that if he found any followers of Jesus there, whether they were men or women, he might bring them to Jerusalem.

So Saul journeyed toward Damascus with this evil purpose in mind. As he drew near the city, suddenly a bright light from heaven shone around him. And he fell to the ground and heard a voice saying to him, "Saul, Saul, why do you persecute me?" Saul asked, "Who are you, Lord?" And the voice replied, "I am Jesus, whom you are persecuting; but rise and go into the city, and it will be told you what you must do."

The men who were with Saul stood speechless from fear. They heard the voice speaking to Saul, but they saw no one. Saul arose from the ground; and when his eyes were opened, he could not see anything. So his companions led him by the hand and brought him into Damascus. And for three days Saul was without sight, and neither ate nor drank anything.

Now there was at Damascus a disciple of Jesus named Ananias. The Lord spoke to him in a vision, saying, "Ananias." And he replied, "Behold, I am here, Lord." And the Lord said to him, "Arise and go to the street that is called Straight, and inquire in the house of Judas for a man of Tarsus by the name of Saul; for behold, he is praying, and he has seen in a vision a man named Ananias coming in and laying his hands on him in order that he might recover his sight."

But Ananias objected, saying, "Lord, I have heard from many about this man, how much evil he has done to your saints at Jerusalem; and here he has authority from the chief priests to bind all who call upon your name." But the Lord commanded Ananias, saying, "Go on, for he is a chosen vessel to me to bear my name before the Gentiles and kings and the children of Israel; for I will show him how greatly he must suffer for my name's sake."

Then Ananias obeyed the word of the Lord. He went out and entered the house where Saul was waiting. And putting his hands on him Ananias said, "Brother Saul, the Lord Jesus who appeared to you in the road by which you came has sent me so that you may recover your sight and be filled with the Holy Spirit." And immediately there fell from his eyes something like scales, and he recovered his sight. Then he arose and was baptized as a disciple of the Lord. His new-found Christian friends gave him food to eat, and he was strengthened.

For several days Saul, who had now become a Christian, stayed with the disciples at Damascus. And in the synagogues of the Jews he began at once to preach Jesus, saying that He was the Son of God. And all who heard him were amazed at the change in Saul, and said, "Is not this the man who destroyed those in Jerusalem who called on the name of Jesus; and who came here with the same intention, to bring the disciples bound to the chief priests?" But Saul increased all the more in strength, and confounded the Jews who lived in Damascus by proving that Jesus was the Christ.

After many days had passed, the Jews conspired to kill this new Christian convert, but their plot became known to Saul. They were watching the gates of the city day and night, so that they might seize him and kill him; but his disciples helped him to escape by taking him under cover of night and lowering him down over the wall in a large basket.

When Saul had returned to Jerusalem he tried to join the disciples there. But they were all afraid of him, because they did not believe that he had really become a disciple. But a kind and generous friend by the name of Barnabas took Saul, and brought him to the apostles, and declared to them how Saul had seen the Lord on the road, and how He had spoken to him, and how he had preached boldly at Damascus in the name of Jesus.

So Saul was accepted by the disciples in Jerusalem as one of their number. He went in and out among them at Jerusalem, preaching

Ananias touched Saul of Tarsus so that he might recover his sight

boldly in the name of the Lord. And he spoke and disputed against the Greek-speaking Jews. These became greatly offended at Saul and planned to kill him. But Saul's Christian brothers learned about this plot, and they conducted him in safety down to Caesarea, and from there sent him off to his native city of Tarsus.

THIRTY

Peter Heals Aeneas and Raises Dorcas

Acts 9:31–43

FOLLOWING the conversion of Saul of Tarsus, the leading persecutor of the Christians, the early Church enjoyed a period of peace and growth. The Churches throughout all Judea and Galilee and Samaria enjoyed a period of peace during which they were built up. And the number of disciples who walked in the fear of the Lord and in the comfort of the Holy Spirit was greatly multiplied.

During this season of growth and change, the apostle Peter made a number of short journeys which had an important influence upon the life of the expanding Church. We are told that as Peter went everywhere, visiting different groups of believers, he came also to the saints or Christians who lived at Lydda, a town located a few miles southeast of Joppa.

There Peter found a man by the name of Aeneas, who had kept his bed for eight long years because he was paralyzed. Peter spoke kindly to the stricken man and said to him, "Aeneas, Jesus Christ makes you well; arise and make your bed." And immediately he got up from his bed and was well. And all who lived at Lydda and the neighboring village of Saron saw how Aeneas had been healed, and they turned to the Lord and became disciples.

About twelve miles from Lydda was the seaport city of Joppa, the modern name of which is Jaffa. In the city of Joppa there lived a disciple by the name of Tabitha, which is the same as the Greek Dorcas or "Gazelle." This Christian woman was known for the many good works and acts of charity which she did. But in those days she suddenly became sick and died. Her friends prepared her body as though for burial, and laid her in an upper room.

Inasmuch as Lydda was near Joppa, and the disciples in Joppa had heard that Peter was in the town near by, they sent two men to him entreating him not to delay to come to them. So Peter immediately rose up and went with them.

When they reached Lydda, the men took Peter at once to the home of Dorcas. He went to the upper room and saw where the dead woman was laid. All the widows gathered around him weeping, and showing the coats and garments which Dorcas had made while she was with them.

But Peter put them all outside, and knelt down and prayed. Then turning to the body he said, "Tabitha, arise." And she opened her eyes, and when she saw Peter, she sat up. And

Peter gave Dorcas his hand

he gave her his hand and pulled her up. Then calling the saints and widows to come in, he presented Dorcas alive again.

This miracle of raising the dead became known throughout all Joppa, and many believed in the Lord Jesus. And Peter stayed in Joppa for many days thereafter with a certain man named Simon, who was a tanner.

The influence of Dorcas remains today, as in the early Church. She believed the Gospel as preached by the apostles, and became a faithful disciple of Christ. She lived a life of holiness and devotion. She was a saint in the true sense of the word. She expressed her faith in loving deeds of compassion and helpfulness.

Dorcas was especially skilled at sewing and making warm and durable garments. She used this ability in the service of her Master, and for the welfare of the poor widows and orphans in her community. All the people whom she helped loved her greatly for her kindness and generosity to them.

The example of this one humble Christian woman has resulted in the organization of numerous Dorcas Societies, and has inspired countless women to render similar service to the poor and needy, in the name and spirit of Christ.

THIRTY-ONE

Peter's Vision on the Housetop

Acts 10:1–48

THIS story of Peter and Cornelius reveals how the first Gentile believers were received into the Christian Church. The reception of Cornelius and the members of his household into the Church marks a turning point in early Christian history, and shows how the Church was preparing to carry the Gospel to everyone.

Cornelius was a Roman soldier stationed at Caesarea. He was a centurion in command of a company of soldiers known as the Italian Band. He was a devout man who feared God with all his household, gave alms generously to the people, and prayed to God always. One afternoon about three o'clock, he saw clearly in a vision an angel of God coming in to him and saying, "Cornelius."

Cornelius was a brave man, but this sight of the angel filled him with fear. He gazed at the angel and said, "What is it, Lord?" The angel said to him, "Your prayers and your alms have come up as a memorial before God. And now send men to Joppa and call for one Simon whose surname is Peter; he is lodging with one Simon a tanner, whose house is by the seaside. He will tell you what to do."

When the angel who spoke to him had departed, Cornelius called two of his servants and a devout soldier from among those that waited on him, and having told them everything, he sent them to Joppa.

The next day, when the messengers from Cornelius were approaching the city of Joppa, Peter went up on the housetop to pray, about the noon hour. He became very hungry and desired something to eat. While his friends were getting the meal ready, Peter fell into a trance and saw heaven opened, and something descending toward him like a great sheet knit at the four corners. It let down to earth, and in it were all kinds of four-footed animals, reptiles, and birds of the air. And there came a voice to him: "Rise, Peter; kill and eat." But Peter refused, saying, "No, Lord; for I have never eaten anything that is common or unclean." The voice spoke to him a second time: "What God has cleansed, do not call that common." This occurred three times; then the sheet was brought up again into heaven.

Now while Peter was very much puzzled as to what this strange vision might mean, behold, the messengers from Cornelius stood at the gate. They had inquired for Simon's house and had asked whether Simon whose surname was Peter was lodging there. And while Peter was deep in thought about the vision, the Spirit said to him, "Behold, three men are inquiring for you. Arise therefore and go down, and go with them without a moment's hesitation; for I have sent them."

Peter went down to the men who had been sent to him and said, "I am the one you are looking for. What is the reason for which you have come?" They replied, "Cornelius the centurion, a just and righteous man, of good reputation among the whole Jewish community, was instructed by a holy angel to send men to ask you to come to his house, and to hear what you will tell him." So he called them in and gave them lodging.

The next morning Peter arose and went with the men, and some of the disciples from Joppa accompanied him. On the following day they arrived at Caesarea. Cornelius was expecting them and had called together his relatives and close friends.

Peter saw something descending toward him filled with all kinds of four-footed animals

As Peter went into his house, Cornelius met him and fell down at his feet and worshiped him. But Peter pulled him up, saying, "Stand up; I myself also am a man." And as he talked with Cornelius, he went in and found that many persons had come together there. And Peter said to them, "You know that it is unlawful for a Jew to keep company with or to pay a visit to anyone of another nation. But God has showed me that I should not call any man common or unclean. So when you sent for me, I came without a moment's hesitation. I ask you then why have you sent for me."

Cornelius then told Peter about the wonderful vision he had seen, and how an angel of the Lord had directed him to send for Peter at Joppa. Cornelius concluded, "So I sent my servants to you at once, and you have been very kind to come. Now therefore we are all here present before God to hear all things that the Lord has commanded you to speak."

Then Peter declared what the vision he had seen on the housetop meant to him. He said, "Now I perceive that God is no respecter of persons, but in every nation anyone who fears Him and whose works are righteous is acceptable to Him." Then Peter told Cornelius and his friends how Jesus went about doing good, and healing all that were oppressed by the devil, for God was with Him. He told how Jesus was put to death on the cross, and how God raised Him on the third day. He described how the risen Lord had appeared to the apostles, and commanded them to preach the Gospel of the forgiveness of sins through faith in the name of Jesus.

While Peter was saying these things, the Holy Spirit fell on all who heard the word. And as many of the Jewish believers as had come with Peter were astonished, because even on the Gentiles was the gift of the Holy Spirit poured out. For they heard them speaking in different tongues and praising God. Then Peter said, "Can anyone forbid the use of water to baptize these people who have received the Holy Spirit just as we have?" And he commanded that they be baptized in the name of the Lord.

THIRTY-TWO

An Angel Delivers Peter From Prison

Acts 12:1–24

ABOUT ten years had passed since the Church in Jerusalem had suffered persecution at the hands of Saul of Tarsus. Now about fourteen years after the resurrection of Jesus, a new persecution was directed against the Christians in Jerusalem. At this time Herod Agrippa I, a vain and cruel man, like his grandfather Herod the Great, was reigning over all Palestine.

Apparently with the hope of gaining favor with the Jews, Herod the king laid cruel hands upon some members of the Church in Jerusalem. First he killed James the brother of John with the sword. This was James the son of Zebedee, one of the fishermen apostles of

Jesus. He was thus the first of the apostles of Jesus to die a martyr's death.

Because Herod saw that this cruel act pleased the Jews, he proceeded to seize Peter also. This happened during the days of Unleavened Bread, the same time of the year that Jesus had been crucified. When he had arrested Peter, he put him in prison, and delivered him to four groups of soldiers, sixteen in all, to keep watch over him; intending after Easter to bring him out to the people. So Peter was kept in prison; but unceasing prayer for him was made to God by the Church.

The very night that Herod meant to bring him out, Peter was sleeping between two soldiers, bound with two chains, and guards before the door were keeping watch over the prison. And behold, the angel of the Lord came upon them, and a light shone in the prison; and he hit Peter on the side and woke him, saying, "Arise up quickly." At once the chains fell off his hands. And the angel said to Peter, "Get dressed and fasten your sandals." And he did so. Then the angel said, "Wrap your cloak about you and follow me." And he went out and followed him. But Peter did not know that what the angel had done was real, but thought he was seeing a vision.

When they had passed the first and the second sentry, they came to the great iron gate leading into the city. This gate opened to them of its own accord, and they went out and walked on through one street; and at once the angel left him. When Peter came to himself, he said, "Now I know for sure that the Lord has sent his angel and has saved me from the hand of Herod, and from all the things the people of the Jews were expecting to happen."

When Peter apprehended that he was free, he went at once to the house of Mary, the mother of John Mark, where many of the Christians were gathered together in prayer.

Peter went out and followed the angel

He knocked at the door of the gate, and a lovely young girl named Rhoda came to answer. Recognizing Peter's voice, she was too overcome with joy to open the gate, but ran in and told the people that Peter was outside.

They did not believe Rhoda was telling the truth, and said to her, "You are mad." But she insisted Peter was really there. They said, "It is his angel." But all this time Peter continued knocking, and when they finally opened the gate, they were astonished to see Peter standing before them. Although they had been praying earnestly for his deliverance, when God answered their prayer they had difficulty believing the wonderful reality of it.

Beckoning to them with his hand to keep still, Peter told them how the Lord had brought him out of the prison. And he directed them to carry the news to James, the brother of Jesus, and to the other Christian brothers. Then Peter departed and went to another place so that he might be safe from the clutches of Herod.

The next morning there was great excitement and consternation among the soldiers as to what had become of Peter. And when Herod had searched for him and could not find him, he was filled with wrath and fury. Calling the guards to him he questioned them thoroughly, and then commanded that they be put to death for allowing Peter to escape.

Then Herod went down from Jerusalem to Caesarea and stayed there until he died a short time later.

THIRTY-THREE

The First Christian Missionaries Sent Forth

Acts 13:1–14:28

BEFORE the risen Lord ascended into heaven, He commissioned His apostles, saying, "But you shall receive power after the Holy Spirit has come upon you; and you shall be witnesses to me both in Jerusalem and in all Judea, and in Samaria and to the uttermost parts of the earth." For a number of years following the ascension of Jesus, the disciples were busy fulfilling the first part of this commission. Now, after sixteen years had passed, the Church commenced its task of carrying the Gospel to "the uttermost parts of the earth."

A strong Church had been founded at Antioch of Syria, more than three hundred miles north of Jerusalem. In this Church at Antioch there were prophets and teachers, Barnabas, Simeon who was called Niger, Lucius of Cyrene, Manaen a member of the court of Herod the tetrarch, and Saul of Tarsus. The Church had become a truly spiritual, prayerful, self-denying, compassionate, consecrated company of Christians.

As they were ministering to the Lord and fasting, the Holy Spirit said to them, "Set aside Barnabas and Saul for me for the work to which I have called them." And when they had fasted and prayed a little longer, they laid their hands in blessing upon Barnabas and Saul and sent them forth as the first Christian missionaries.

So, being sent forth by the Holy Spirit, Barnabas and Saul left for the seaport of Seleucia; and from there they sailed to the island of Cyprus. When they arrived at the port of Salamis, they preached the word of God in the synagogues of the Jews. And they had also John Mark to guide them.

When they had gone through the whole island as far as Paphos, they met a certain sorcerer, a Jewish false prophet whose name was Bar-Jesus. He was with the deputy of the country, Sergius Paulus, a man of prudence, who called for Barnabas and Saul desiring to hear the word of God.

But Elymas the sorcerer (that is what his name means) withstood them, seeking to turn away the deputy from the faith. Then Saul, who is also called Paul after this, filled with the Holy Spirit, gazed intently at Elymas and said, "You are full of all craft and mischief; you are a child of the Devil; you are an enemy of all righteousness. When will you stop perverting the right ways of the Lord? And now behold, the hand of the Lord shall punish you, and you shall be blind and unable to see the sun for a while. Immediately there fell upon him a mist and darkness, and he went about looking for someone to lead him by the hand. Then when the deputy Sergius Paulus saw what had happened, he believed; for he was astonished at the power of the Lord.

Then Paul and his companions cast off from Paphos, and came to Perga in Pamphylia. There John Mark left them and returned to Jerusalem. Going on from Perga they came to Antioch in Pisidia. There in the synagogue on the sabbath day Paul preached his first recorded Christian sermon.

But the next sabbath, the Jews stirred up the devout and honorable women and chief men of the city to persecute Paul and Barnabas and expel them from the district. The missionaries then went to Iconium and so preached in the synagogue there that a great number of Jews and Greeks believed. But the unbelieving Jews stirred up more trouble and sought to stone Paul and Barnabas. So they fled for safety to Lystra and Derbe, cities of Lycaonia.

At Lystra, Paul healed a man who had been crippled from birth. As a result, the heathen people regarded Paul and Barnabas as gods who had come to them in the likeness of men. But Paul assured them that they were only men, and proclaimed to them the truth of the living God who made the heaven and the earth.

While Paul and Barnabas were at Lystra, troublemaking Jews from Antioch and Iconium came and persuaded the people to turn against the missionaries. So they stoned Paul and dragged him out of the city, supposing him to be dead. But when the disciples gathered around him, he rose up and went back into the city. On the next day he departed with Barnabas to Derbe.

When they had preached the gospel to that city and had made many believe, they returned to Lystra and to Iconium and to Antioch. On these return visits they gave the souls of the disciples renewed strength, and exhorted them to continue in the faith, saying that we must through many tribulations enter the kingdom of God. And when they had ordained elders for them in every Church, with prayer and fasting, they commanded them to the Lord in whom they believed.

Then Paul and Barnabas passed through Pisidia, and came again to Pamphylia. And when they had preached the word in Perga, they went to Attalia. From there they sailed back to the home base at Antioch, where they had been commended to the grace of God for

They arrived at the port of Salamis to preach the word of God

the work which they had fulfilled. And when they had come, they gathered the Church together and related all that God had done with them, and how He had opened the door of faith to the Gentiles. And they remained for some time in Antioch with the disciples.

THIRTY-FOUR

A Midnight Prayer Meeting in Prison

Acts 15:36–16:40

Paul's second missionary journey was begun about three years after his first journey was completed. Paul suggested to Barnabas that they return and visit the Churches they had founded on their first journey. Barnabas wanted to take with them John Mark. But Paul did not want to take Mark because he had deserted them at Pamphylia on the first journey. A sharp disagreement arose between them and they separated from each other. Barnabas took Mark and went off to Cyprus. Paul chose a new companion, Silas, and they set forth to revisit the Churches in Syria and Cilicia.

So Paul came again to Derbe and to Lystra, the place where he had been stoned. There he found a disciple, named Timothy, whose mother was a Jewish believer and whose father was a Greek. Timothy was well regarded by the Christians at Lystra and Iconium. So Paul asked him to join them.

They went throughout Phrygia and Galatia, but they had been forbidden by the Holy Spirit to preach the Gospel in Asia. When they had come to Mysia, they intended to go into Bithynia, but again the Spirit of Jesus did not permit them to. So passing by Mysia, they went down to the ancient city of Troas, or Troy. There a vision appeared to Paul in the night. A man from Macedonia stood over him and implored him: "Come over into Macedonia and help us." And after Paul had seen the vision, they immediately decided to go to Macedonia, understanding from the vision that God had called them to preach the Gospel there. Another companion, Luke, joined Paul and Silas and Timothy at Troas.

Casting out therefore from Troas, they sailed straight to Samothrace, and the next day to Neapolis, and from there to Philippi, which was the principal city of Macedonia and a Roman colony. The four Christian missionaries had now come from Asia to the continent of Europe. They stayed in Philippi for a few days, and on the sabbath day they went out of the city by the gate that led to the river side, where they hoped to find a place of prayer. They sat down in that pleasant place and spoke to the women who had come there.

One of these good women was named Lydia; she came from the city of Thyatira in Asia Minor. She was a successful businesswoman, a seller of purple goods, and a worshiper of God. The Lord opened her heart to heed the Gospel as it was spoken by Paul.

And when she was baptized, with the members of her household, she graciously invited the missionaries to lodge in her house. This they were happy to do. So Lydia was the first Christian convert in Philippi and on the continent of Europe.

Later, as the missionaries were going to prayer, they were met by a poor maid who was able to foretell future events and who brought her masters much gain through her soothsaying. She followed Paul and his companions, crying, "These men are the servants of the most high God, who showed us the way of salvation." She continued to do this for many days. Paul was disturbed by her plight and turned and said to the evil spirit, "I command you in the name of Jesus Christ to come out of her." And it came out that very hour.

When her greedy masters saw that the hope of their gain was gone, they laid hold upon Paul and Silas and dragged them into the market place before the rulers. They brought them to the magistrates and said, "These men, being Jews, are causing a great deal of trouble in our city. They teach customs which it is not lawful for Romans either to tolerate or to observe." The crowd joined in reviling Paul and Silas, and the magistrates tore off their garments and commanded them to be beaten. And when many stripes had been laid upon their backs, they were thrown into prison, and the jailer was charged to keep them safely. Having received his orders, the jailer thrust them into the inner prison and made their feet fast in the stocks.

At midnight Paul and Silas prayed and sang praises to God, and the other prisoners listened to them. Suddenly there was a great earthquake, so that the foundations of the prison were shaken; and immediately all the

The jailer fell down before Paul and Silas

doors were opened and everyone's chains were loosened. The keeper of the prison awoke and saw the prison doors open; he drew his sword and was on the verge of killing himself, because he supposed that all the prisoners had fled.

But Paul cried loudly, "Do not harm yourself, for we are all here." And the jailer called for a light and ran in trembling with fear, and fell down before Paul and Silas, and brought them out and said, "Sirs, what must I do to be saved?" And they said to him, "Believe in the Lord Jesus Christ, and you shall be saved, and the members of your household."

Then Paul and Silas spoke the word of the Lord to the jailer and to all the members of his household. And this grateful man took the missionaries that same hour of the night and washed their wounds. The missionaries in turn baptized the jailer and the members of his family. Then the jailer took Paul and Silas to his home, and gave them food; and he rejoiced with all his household that he believed in God.

But when day came, the magistrates sent the police, saying, "Let those men go." And the keeper of the prison relayed these words to Paul, saying, "The magistrates have sent to have me let you go; now therefore depart, and go in peace." But Paul's sense of justice wouldn't let him drop the matter so easily.

So Paul replied to the jailer, "They have beaten us openly uncondemned, even though we are Roman citizens, and have thrown us into prison; and now are they trying to thrust us out in secret? Not at all! Let them come themselves and take us out."

The police told these words to the magistrates, and they were afraid when they heard that Paul and Silas were Roman citizens; so they came in person and begged their forgiveness. And they brought them out and invited them to quit the city of Philippi. So Paul and Silas went out of the prison, and went again into the hospitable home of Lydia. And when they had seen the Christian brothers, they comforted them and told them to stand fast in the faith, then took their departure.

THIRTY-FIVE

Paul's Mighty Works in Ephesus

Acts 19:8–20:1

HAVING completed his second missionary journey, Paul remained in Antioch for about a year, then started on his third journey. He traveled through the whole country of Galatia and Phrygia, strengthening all the disciples. Passing along the upper coasts, Paul came to the great city of Ephesus, where he ministered in many different ways for about three years.

He began his preaching in the synagogue of the Jews who lived there, and for the space of three months spoke boldly, reasoning and persuading concerning the kingdom of God. But when some of his Jewish hearers were defiant and unbelieving, and began to speak evil of the way of Christ to the people, Paul left them and took the disciples who did believe with him. He went to a school in the city, the school of Tyrannus, where he continued to teach every day for two years. During this time great numbers of people who lived in Asia Minor heard the word of the Lord, both Jews and Greeks.

And God worked special miracles by the hands of Paul, so that handkerchiefs or aprons which were carried away from his body to the sick caused diseases to leave them and evil spirits to depart from them.

Many of the new converts came to Paul to confess and declare their misdeeds. And many of those who practiced magic brought their books together and burned them in the presence of everyone. And they estimated the worth of these books and found it to be fifty thousand pieces of silver. So the word of God grew and prevailed mightily.

After these stirring events Paul determined to pass through Macedonia and Achaia and to go to Jerusalem, saying, "After I have been there, I must also see Rome." So he sent into Macedonia two of his assistants, Timothy and Erastus, but he himself stayed in Asia for a time.

Soon there arose a great commotion over the gospel of Christ that Paul had been preaching. In the city of Ephesus there was a great temple for the worship of Diana. A huge idol of Diana stood in the temple, and images of this idol were made and sold to the worshipers to carry with them. A man by the name of Demetrius, a silversmith, made these silver shrines of Diana, and brought much gain to the craftsmen who shared the business.

Demetrius was greatly disturbed by the effects of Paul's teachings because the sale of images of Diana was falling off. So he called his fellow craftsmen together and said to them, "Sirs, you know that from this craft we derive our wealth. Moreover, you see and hear that not alone at Ephesus but almost throughout all Asia this Paul has persuaded and turned away a very large number of people, saying that gods made with hands are no gods at all. So that there is danger not only that this craft of ours may lose favor, but also that the

Many who practiced magic burned their books in the presence of everyone

temple of the great goddess Diana may come to naught, and that she may be dethroned and her magnificence destroyed, she whom all Asia and the world worship."

When they heard this they were filled with anger, and cried out, "Great is Diana of the Ephesians!" And the whole city was filled with confusion; and they seized Gaius and Aristarchus, men from Macedonia who were Paul's companions in travel, and rushed with one accord into the theater. Paul wanted to go in among the people but the disciples persuaded him not to. And certain of the Asians, who were friends of Paul, sent to him, urging him not to venture into the theater.

Some therefore cried one thing, and some another; for the whole assembly was in confusion, and most of them did not know why they had come together. Part of the crowd wanted to hear from Alexander, whom the Jews had put forward. But when they realized that he was a Jew, they raised an uproar and for about two hours they all shouted with one voice, "Great is Diana of the Ephesians!"

Finally the town clerk calmed the crowd and said, "Men of Ephesus, who is there among you who does not know that the city of the Ephesians is the guardian of the great goddess Diana, and of the sacred image which fell down from Jupiter? Seeing then that these things cannot be denied, you ought to be orderly and do nothing reckless. For you have brought here men who are neither robbers of temples nor blasphemers of your goddess."

As the people listened to this wise counsel, the town clerk continued, "If then Demetrius and the craftsmen with him wish to state a grievance against anyone, the courts are open and there are deputies; let them sue one another. But if you want something with regard to other matters, it shall be decided in a lawful assembly. For we are in danger of being called in question for today's commotion, there being no good reason by which we can account for this uproar." And when he had thus spoken, he dismissed the assembly.

Afterwards, Paul called the disciples to him, embraced them, then left for Macedonia.

THIRTY-SIX

Paul's Journey to Rome

Acts 28:11–31

At Ephesus, on his third missionary journey, Paul determined to carry the Gospel to Rome. In the providence of God, he was permitted to make the journey, but by what a long and difficult and dangerous route!

Leaving Ephesus, Paul visited Greece, and returned to Miletus where he said farewell to the Ephesian elders.

He then returned to Jerusalem, where he was arrested and persecuted by the Jews. He was tried before the Jewish council, but rescued from violence by the Roman authorities.

A company of Roman soldiers conducted

him in safety to Caesarea, where he was arraigned before Felix, the Roman governor.

Paul remained in prison in Caesarea for two years, then was arraigned before the new governor Porcius Festus. The Christian apostle exercised his right as a Roman citizen and appealed to Caesar, the Roman emperor. Hence Festus decided to send Paul to Rome.

While yet in Caesarea, Paul appeared before the Jewish king Herod Agrippa II, before whom he made a notable defense. Agrippa declared that Paul might have been set at liberty had he not appealed to Caesar.

Finally the voyage to Rome was begun. In custody of the Augustan band of Roman soldiers, Paul was taken on board a ship which set sail for Italy.

They were overtaken by a terrible storm, and the ship was wrecked on the island of Melita, or Malta. As by a miracle, Paul and all the others on board the stricken vessel escaped safely to land.

After three months they set out in a ship of Alexandria which had wintered in the island, and whose sign was Castor and Pollux. Landing at Syracuse, they lodged there for three days. And from there they went to Rhegium; and after one day a south wind began to blow, and on the following day they came to Puteoli, on the coast of Italy.

There Paul found Christian disciples who invited him to stay with them for seven days. And so Paul, the intrepid missionary of the Cross, went on to Rome. The Christian brothers in Rome, when they heard that Paul was coming, went to meet him at the Forum of Appius and the Three Taverns. On seeing them Paul thanked God and took courage

Paul preached the kingdom of God to all who came to him

At Rome, Paul was permitted to stay by himself, with a soldier to guard him.

After three days he called together the chiefs of the Jews; and when they had come together, he said to them, "Men and brothers, though I did nothing against the people or against the customs of our fathers, yet I was delivered prisoner from Jerusalem into the hands of the Romans, who, when they examined me, would have let me go, because there was no reason for sentencing me to death. But when the Jews complained, I was constrained to appeal to Caesar—not that I had anything of which to accuse my nation. It is for this reason that I have called you together to speak with you, since it is on account of the hope of Israel that I am bound with this chain."

And the leaders said to Paul, "We have neither received letters from Judea about you, nor have any of the brothers who have come here had any evil to speak about you. But we desire to hear what you have to say; for as concerns this sect, we know that everywhere it is spoken against."

When they had appointed a day to hear Paul, a great many came to him at his lodging. And Paul expounded the kingdom of God to them, from morning till evening, trying to persuade them concerning Jesus, both from the law of Moses and from the prophets. And some believed his words, and others did not believe. So, when they did not agree among themselves, they departed, after Paul had made one statement: "Well did the Holy Spirit say to your fathers through Isaiah the prophet:

'Go to this people and say,
"Hearing you shall hear, and shall not understand;
And seeing you shall see and not perceive;

For the heart of this people has become heavy,
And their ears are dull of hearing,
And their eyes they have closed;
Lest they should see with their eyes,
And hear with their ears,
And understand with their hearts
And should be converted, and I should heal them." '

Let it be known to you therefore that this salvation of God is sent to the Gentiles; they will hear and receive it."

And Paul lived in Rome two whole years in his own rented house where he graciously received all who came to him, preaching the kingdom of God and teaching those things which concern the Lord Jesus Christ openly and freely.

On the night of His farewell fellowship with His disciples in the upper room in Jerusalem, Jesus had said to them, "Truly, truly I say to you, he that believes in me will also do the works that I do; and greater works than these shall he do, because I go to my Father." And then, just before the risen Lord ascended into heaven, He said to His apostles, "But you shall receive power after the Holy Spirit has come upon you; and you shall be witnesses to me both in Jerusalem and in all Judea, and in Samaria and to the uttermost parts of the earth."

The Book of Acts records the partial fulfillment of the Lord's commission and promise. This history of the early Church records the acts of Christ's apostles, the acts of the Holy Spirit, the works the apostles did because the living Lord was working in and through them, and because they remembered His sacred promise, "Lo, I am with you always, even to the end of the world."

About the Author

J. HAROLD GWYNNE, D.D., is a native of western Pennsylvania. He holds degrees from The College of Wooster, Wooster, Ohio, Princeton Theological Seminary, and Princeton University Graduate College. He has been an ordained minister of the Presbyterian Church, U.S.A., since 1927, and is the pastor of Grace Presbyterian Church, Lakewood, Ohio. Dr. Gwynne has contributed widely to the devotional, educational, and religious life of the Church through his books on Christian living, his worship program materials, and his devotional articles and meditations.

About the Artist

STEELE SAVAGE was born in Michigan. He attended the Art Institute of Chicago and the Slade School in London; he studied further in both Vienna and Paris. He has designed sets for a number of Broadway theatrical productions and is well known as a furniture designer. Among the more than forty books Mr. Savage has illustrated are the *Iliad* and other classics. He is noted for his historical illustration. Mr. Savage lives in New York City.

THIS BOOK WAS SET IN TIMES ROMAN AND PERPETUA TYPES BY WESTCOTT & THOMSON.
IT WAS PRINTED BY COPIFYER LITHOGRAPH CORPORATION ON
PERKINS AND SQUIER SPECIAL OFFSET MADE BY P. H. GLATFELTER COMPANY.
THE BINDING WAS DONE AT THE PRESS OF THE WORLD PUBLISHING COMPANY.
TYPOGRAPHY AND DESIGN ARE BY ABE LERNER.

4 5 6 7 8 9 10 66 65 64 63 62 61